METHODIST MAVERICK

DANIEL BRAXTON TURNEY (1848-1926)

GEORGE WHITE

Wasteland Press

www.wastelandpress.net
Shelbyville, KY USA

Methodist Maverick:
Daniel Braxton Turney (1848-1926)
by George White

First Printing – September 2020
ISBN: 978-1-68111-373-9
Library of Congress Control Number: 2020916462

Printed in the U.S.A.

0   1   2   3   4   5

PREFACE

"Maverick-an independent-minded person who refuses to abide by the dictates of...a group; dissenter."* Daniel Braxton Turney was a maverick in his time (1848-1926). He was an opinionated Methodist preacher who rebelled against the supervision of bishops, but often had to supervise churches in southern Illinois. He was a pioneer of prohibition who guzzled coffee and died of liver cancer. He was born in a log cabin, lived in the governor's mansion in the Washington Territory and twice failed as U.S. presidential candidate for the United Christian Party.

At 32, Turney was national Polemic for the Methodist Protestant denomination in Washington, D.C., had dozens of scholarly articles published by national journals and had been booted out of half a dozen churches in Illinois, Ohio and West Virginia. He was a general of ideas who often marched without an army; a pulpiteer in search of his next pulpit; a woman suffrage spokesman, who neglected his own wife.

D.B. Turney was lauded, laughed at; followed and ignored; respected and ridiculed; fondly remembered and widely forgotten. He was a maverick and also my great-grandfather. I offer his biography based on 30 years of research. When known, names and places are

---

* *The American Heritage Dictionary*, Houghton Mifflin Co., Boston (1991), p 773

historically accurate, embellished by my experience and imagination. Thanks for the help from dedicated historians and my wife Martha!

CHAPTER ONE

The Oregon Trail
July-Aug. 1861

The westbound stage bounced, crawled over a boulder, tilted toward the ravine, then righted itself. The eleven passengers, exhausted from two-weeks of bounces, jolts and heat, hardly noticed. They were packed in like sardines. The four adults and seven children no longer gazed at the stunning landscapes flowing by. Eyes were glazed by lack of sleep. Minds were numbed, except for Leander Jay S. Turney, whose thoughts raced like a prairie jackrabbit outrunning a coyote, His wife Elizabeth cradled their wiggly three-year-old, but did not know how to comfort her twitchy husband. He had been like this since they left Illinois two weeks ago. He paid little attention to the scenery or his family. Elizabeth sighed. At least Fran was asleep at last. Ten-year-old Johnny leaned over to poke Fran, but was stopped by his mother's stern stare. Seven-year-old Margaret giggled that her brother got caught. L. Jay frantically scribbled ideas on a scrap of paper and missed it all.

So did eldest son Dan, 13, who was above it all, up on the driver's bench, hunched over a book. He was supposed to keep an eye on their belongings strapped atop the coach, but reading was more interesting.

The driver wondered why the boy was such a bookworm and asked, "Hey, tenderfoot, what you reading?"

Dan looked up, "It's a book my Grandpa gave me when we left Illinois."

"Does your book have a name?"

Dan carefully kept his place and turned his copy of "Pilgrim's Progress" toward the driver.

He glanced quickly, then shrugged, "That's OK, I can't read. You be lucky. I never knew my grampa and he shore never gave me no books."

"Grandpa Parish has lots of books," Dan said, "but my dad has more."

"What's he do?" the driver asked.

"He was a lawyer back in Illinois. But out in the Washington Territory, he's going to be Secretary of State and acting Governor."

"Both?"

"That's what Abe Lincoln asked him to do." Dan said proudly.

The driver guided the horses around another fallen boulder and glanced at the boy, "Your Pa's going to be the Big Boss Man; a right Big Whig!"

Dan shook his head, "L. Jay S. Turney never was a Whig. He used to be a Democrat, but now he's a Republican."

"Sounds like he can't make up his mind! You never know. I once thought I'd be stuck on our tiny farm, but here I am living in the wide-open spaces of the Oregon Trail!" He tightened the reins as they rounded a bend. "This here Trail is about as young as you are, boy!"

"Daniel Braxton is my name!"

"Like the guy in bible who got thrown to the lions?" The driver stuck his hand, "I'm Thomas, like the bible guy who doubted."

Dan's hand was swallowed in Thomas's rough grip. Remembering his manners, he said, "Glad to meet you Thomas."

"I be honored. Never met a governor's son before. But we're going to have to say our goodbyes soon. Just beyond that rise up yonder, we'll see the Columbia. She's a mighty river. You'll see for yourself when we get to Umatilla."

"Is that in the Washington Territory?" Dan asked.

"Nope. You've got a far piece to go before you get to the Territory. Guess Mr. Governor man is headed for the capital.... I forget what it's called."

"Olympia!" Dan answered.

"Umatilla, Oregon is as far as I go. Then, back to Boise."

Dan squinted into the setting sun and gripped the rail as they rounded a curve. The dusty stage picked up speed bouncing downhill into the town. The horses sniffed the air, smelling the river and pranced into the Umatilla Landing. It was barely a town; the population doubled whenever a steamboat docked.

The driver climbed down, tied the horses to the hitching post and opened the stage door with a flourish, announcing, "Umatilla Landing!" Two men, two women and six children staggered, stumbled and jumped down to the solid ground, joining Dan, who said, "We finally made it!"

"Not there, yet," his father L. Jay S. Turney, corrected. "This is just the Columbia River landing; we're still a long way from Olympia, Washington. Ten-year-old Johnny Turney complained, "I'm sick and tired of riding. I feel like a turtle trapped in a stage coach shell." His uncle, John T. Knox stretched his legs and ruffled the boy's hair, "That was the best ride ever- The Oregon Trail on a Concord Coach!!"

"You wouldn't have so much fun traveling, if you had to care for seven children!" Elizabeth Turney chided, while juggling her infant daughter.

Knox shrugged, "You're probably right, Sis."

"You know she is, John! We herd the kids and you make new friends at every stage station from St. Louis to Fort Hall," Sarah Knox said.

"Let's go meet some new friends," Knox laughed as he hurried to catch up with L. Jay. Dan and his brother Johnny dashed to the boat dock and unleashed hours of pent-up energy by throwing rocks out into the river. Dan, with a three-year age advantage, won these throwing contests. But Johnny was gaining on him.

L. Jay scolded his boys, "Daniel, Johnny, stop dawdling! We need to get some food and find out where we sleep. Tomorrow, we'll get enough of the river. It will be an early start!"

"When do we sail?" Johnny asked.

"No sailing," his father answered. "We **steam** out at 7am."

The 6am warning whistle shattered the morning stillness. Startled children woke. Adults hurried to finish their meager breakfasts. The second whistle from *The Colonel Wright* blasted at 6:45am. Leander and John pushed through the crowd funneling to the boarding gate. Elizabeth Turney and Sarah Knox guided the youngest children, but there was no holding back the Turney boys. They raced past L. Jay and thundered up the narrow ramp. Johnny beat Dan to the top, but both had to wait for L. Jay. He had the tickets. Once admitted, they rushed to the railing and stared into the deep green water, churning down below them. Dan looked across to the rock cliffs on the other side, did a mental calculation and announced, "It's not as big as the mighty Mississippi!"

Their precocious 14-year-old cousin Frances Knox crowded in next to Dan and corrected him, "Out here they call the Columbia River the Amazon of the west!"

"That may well be," Dan retorted, "but I've seen both rivers and the Mississippi is bigger! I've also seen a map and it's also much longer." Frances flipped her hair and stomped back to her mother.

Passengers crowded the deck benches as the steamer began a smooth westward ride downriver. L. Jay leaned back and put his boots on the lowest rail, "John, this is the way to travel!!" Except for the churn of the wheel in the water behind them, it was silent. After lunch, Dan standing at the front of the boat, noticed a change. The river narrowed and turned violent. The Columbia began jerking and pounding the steamship. "What's happening?" he asked a boatman, who was coiling a rope.

"We're entering the Dalles Rapids. Dangerous waters!" Seeing the look on Dan's face, he added, "We know where the rocks are and before it gets too turbulent, we'll dock the ship and send you on a safe land portage around the rapids." Soon the passengers were packed into three stagecoaches for the winding journey above and beside the Columbia. Their luggage trailed behind in an overloaded wagon. Looking down, they saw the river churning and twisting like a mighty snake. Dan had never seen the Mississippi do that, but he wouldn't tell his cousin Frances. The Turney brothers nicknamed her 'Fancy Frances".

The stagecoach portage eventually led them down to The Dalles, a bustling river town. L. Jay told his boys, "Tonight, we sleep in a real bed!" But that didn't happen. The boys slept on the bare floor and their sisters slept in the soft bed with their parents. The next day the eleven Illinois travelers boarded another steamer and churned their way west to the mouth of the Cowlitz River. When he disembarked, L. Jay hurried to the station. He bargained with the clerk for passage up the Cowlitz. Waving a handful of tickets in his hand, he told the family, "We're in luck. We're just in time to catch a steamer going north." He pointed to it. "It's not much to look at, but they've got room for us and our luggage." Elizabeth whispered a prayer of thanks. She knew it was more than luck that a boat had been waiting for them. L. Jay and John oversaw the transfer of luggage as the family boarded. They chugged north up the Cowlitz River. When they reached the shabby destination dock, Elizabeth wished she had prayed harder.

There were no stage coaches available for the last leg of their trip to Olympia. The station master said, "Sorry Mr. Turney, this big freight wagon and those six mules is the best we got."

L. Jay protested, "There are only two benches, barely room for the women and children. Where will the rest of us sit? On our luggage!"

"Reckon that's what you'll have to do!" the agent retorted.

"That will not do. I am the new governor of this territory and it would not be proper for me to ride into the capitol on this poor excuse for transportation!"

"Mr. Governor. It's the wagon, or it's all of you wading through the mud to Olympia. You keep hassling me and I will double your price. Or maybe you'd like to drive the mule team yourself, so you could sit on that comfy seat up front."

L. Jay was ready to explode when John Knox stepped in, "Sir, we're sorry for the misunderstanding. Please bear with the governor. It's been a long and arduous journey. We'll make do with what's available.

The agent was mollified and said, "OK. OK. Billy will help you load your stuff after he hitches up the mules." He leaned in so close that Knox smelled the onions on his breath, "Let me give your governor friend some advice, 'If he ever wants to be elected again, he better show a tad more kindness to ordinary folks!'"

Dan helped Billy heft a big crate onto the wagon bed. John and L. Jay groaned under the weight of a trunk full of law books. Seven trips later the Turney/Knox belongings were stacked on the wagon beside the sacks of grain for the mules. After a meager meal served by Billy's wife, the travelers climbed onto the wagon. Elizabeth sat on the front bench with the driver. Her girls crowded in beside her. Sarah Knox and her three children squeezed in on the second bench. L. Jay sat on his trunk of books, across from John Knox, who was struggling to find room for his long legs. Dan and John were wedged in next to the biggest pile of suitcases, bags and boxes. Frances Knox sat queenlike on her bench and waved at the boys.

Billy surveyed his passengers and asked, "All aboard?" Elizabeth, who was closest said, "We're ready." With a crack of his whip, Billy shouted, "Giddy-up!!" The wagon jerked forward as they began the hardest part of their journey. Mules. Rain. Mud. Getting stuck. Roadblocks. Mud and mules.

Rain pelted them for hours. Humans and mules were soaked to the bone. Billy cursed the rain and cursed the mules. Elizabeth covered little Lucy's ears. But after the second day of rain she was ready to abandon her strict Methodist upbringing and curse the rain, the mules and the mud. They longed for the luxury of the steamboat. Johnny confessed to Dan, "I was a fool to bellyache about the stagecoach back in the desert!"

The steep road became hilly and rough as they climbed up toward the Cowlitz mountain. Huge fir and pine trees lined their path. They crested the ridge and for seven hours crawled along in the mud, often axle deep. They were stopped by a tree, which had fallen across the road.

Billy asked Elizabeth to hold the reins. He grabbed an axe from under his seat, climbed down and chopped away at the tree. L. Jay and John jumped down and helped Billy push the log to the side of the road.

The men were spattered with mud as they climbed back on the wagon. Elizabeth gladly surrendered the reins to the driver. But when Billy shouted, "Giddy-up", nothing happened. The mules refused to budge. Dan watched closely as the mule master cracked his whip and shouted repeatedly. Finally, reacting to the sting of the whip, the mules moved. Billy sighed, "My mules are strong, but stubborn. With the rains, we have to use six mules to pull the same wagon that four could pull in dry weather. My Pappy used to say, 'Choosing a good mule takes more thought than choosing a wife. The two mules I added today aren't my favorites, but I'll teach them to work."

Night dropped a curtain of darkness over them, as they entered a forest so dense and trees so tall, they felt like coal miners in a tunnel scented by pine needles and mule sweat. They groped through the blackness, wet clothes clinging to them and hunger gnawing at them. An owl's hoot startled the mules and the children. Billy jerked the reins and cursed the owl. The mules stubbornly drug the heavy wagon through ponds of water. The lead mule sank in the mud, then floundered helplessly, L. Jay, John and Dan jumped off the wagon and waded through the mud to push, pull and coax the mule out of the deep hole. The mule churned his legs and John warned Dan, "Watch out!" Somehow, they got back to solid footing. Dan's heart was still racing when he climbed onto the wagon. Frances wanted to smirk at how muddy he was, but she was too wet to care, Billy let the mules rest for a few minutes before cracking his whip again.

They emerged from the forest tunnel into a clearing and a rough cabin. "It's Drew's Station!" Billy yelled. "That's a sight for sore eyes! Food and rest at last." Once inside, they crowded around a roaring fire, while Mrs. Drew cooked a simple hot meal. They slept on dry blankets and piles of needles on the rough flooring.

The next morning, after a quick breakfast, they re-harnessed the mules, climbed back on the wagon and resumed their journey down the old road into what Billy called 'The Cowlitz Prairie.' The prairie was dotted with old farmsteads, log cabins and rail fences. Halfway through, they passed a crumbling, abandoned church building. Billy scolded the mules for their slow progress. "We have to make better time if we're to reach the next station tonight!" Traveling through thick timber, they reached the Newakum River. The bridge Billy had expected to cross had been washed away. They searched for a new crossing. The driver and L. Jay disagreed about which way to go. Billy prevailed, grumbling to himself, "I may not hold the reins to the Territory, but I have the reins to my team."

He found a place to ford the river and turned the team into the water. They left a muddy trail in the water as they crossed. The river-washed wagon climbed up the bank onto another muddy prairie road. They struggled through a deeply rutted path until they reached rolling hills with some timber. Billy pointed ahead, "The bridge is still there! Indians call this Skookum Chuck."

Dan asked, "Did the Indians name everything around here?"

"Sure did. This was all their country until we came along." Dan had overheard his father talking with his uncle about problems with the Indians in the Territory. Dan wondered if it was right to take their land.

He asked the driver, "What Indian tribes were here?"

Billy answered "I think Yakima, Cayuse and Nez Pierce lived in these parts. I don't know for sure, maybe you should ask the governor. Not many years ago, there was a big war with the Indians down along the Columbia."

Dan scratched his head. Wars and fighting troubled him. Now the whole country was at war with itself over slavery. Two of his older friends back in Illinois had enlisted to fight for the Union. Dan wondered, 'What if I was 18, instead of 13?' He was lost in thought.

Billy was not lost. He knew his way through this timber road. The road bed was solid and they were making good time. But the sun sank faster than Billy could drive. They settled for lodging seven miles shy of Olympia.

A bright August morning welcomed them as they packed-up to begin their last day on the road. The wagon rolled across another prairie and reached a little village. Dan asked Billy, "What's the Indian name for this place?"

"Tumwater," he answered. "It means 'water falls'.

Dan surveyed the De Chutes River's churning rapids and waterfalls, "Well named!!" Flour mills and saw mills were scattered along the river, tapping the water's energy. The travelers crossed the river and reached the top of the ridge. Johnny stood and excitedly pointed toward the snowy mountains in the distance. Olympia was within sight. The bright sun shimmered on mountain snow above and the Puget Sound water below. Elizabeth uttered a silent prayer, asking God to shine on their new home. L. Jay was itching to get to work. Dan was not sure what to expect.

CHAPTER TWO

Olympia, Washington
Aug 16, 1861

They found the governor's mansion on Main and 11th Street. The house was a new one-and-a-half story clapboard with a front porch and an addition jutting off the back side. L. Jay said, "John, I told you it would be big enough for both families."

"Look at all the yard space!" Sarah Knox exclaimed, "Room for two gardens." Elizabeth nodded, then warned, "Children, clean off your boots and shoes before you go inside. That goes for you, too," she told the men. They toured both wings of the house and decided the Knox family would move into the side section in back with the Turneys in front. The kitchen would be shared. By the time they unloaded everything, it was dark. Exhausted, they slept wherever they could find places among their luggage.

Their cold breakfast was interrupted by a knock on the front door. "L. Jay, go see who that is," Elizabeth said.

He was greeted by two well-dressed men. "Mr. Turney, welcome to Olympia. I am George Barnes and this is Elwood Evans. We represent the town council." Both shook his hand. "We hope your family finds the accommodations adequate." Evans handed him a food basket.

He thanked them and said. "Elizabeth, would you come meet our guests?" She hurried over, wiping her hands with a towel and apologizing that they had no coffee to offer.

"Don't fret, Mrs. Turney. There is a small can of coffee in the basket my wife prepared," Barnes said.

"I look forward to meeting her," Elizabeth replied.

Elwood said, "Mr. Acting Governor, why don't I give you a tour of the capitol on Monday morning?"

"I will be there!" L. Jay said.

True to his word, Elwood Evans met Acting Governor Turney at the Capitol on Monday morning. "You have two jobs but there's only one office up on the second floor. Can I show you?" Evans turned to Dan and Johnny, "You boys up to a little climbing and exploring?"

"Yes," the boys chorused. Johnny asked, "Can we go up to the cupola?"

"I'll show you how to get up there, after I show your father his office and the pile of work waiting for him." The boys raced up the stairway, followed by the two men, who were deep in conversation. L. Jay began to unfold his elaborate plans to guide the Washington Territory. Evans listened attentively, but the rambunctious brothers, interrupted. Evans said, "Sir, let me show the boys the secret door to the cupola, then you can enlighten me further."

Dan and Johnny raced up the narrow staircase to the cupola. "Wow, look at the view!" Dan exclaimed as they ran around the balcony. "Water everywhere. Those mountains over there look like they're holding up the clouds. Did you ever see so many pine trees?"

Johnny piped in, "Some of those trees are taller than this building!"

"Look at that clearing and all those stumps. I bet they built this capitol with those pine trees." Dan said.

"Bet they had to saw them up first." Johnny cracked. He bolted back to the stairway, "Beat you down!" Dan didn't rise to the bait, but circled the balcony again, trying to spot their new house. He wondered which road went to the school house. His mother told them they would start school soon. Dan sauntered back down to the office.

L. Jay told the boys, "Mr. Elwood has offered to walk you two back to the house. I have a pile of work to get started on." He could barely see over the piles of papers, forms and letters. As a lawyer, Turney was no stranger to paperwork. Before the day was over, he realized how many decisions had been delayed and how many unhappy constituents wanted for answers. One issue kept resurfacing- relocating the state capitol. Port Townsend wanted it. Tacoma and Steilacoom thought they deserved it. But a letter from Vancouver made the strongest argument for a move and warned him to act quickly. The missive concluded by announcing that a delegation from Vancouver would arrive by ship on Friday to make their case.

On Friday, Elizabeth sent Dan to the capitol with a packed lunch for Leander. "He missed lunch while waiting for the Vancouver delegation." Dan grabbed the bag and ran to the capitol. He was winded by the time he burst into the second-floor office.

"Dad, here's your lunch." L. Jay thanked him and eagerly bit into the fresh-baked bread. He'd hardly swallowed his first bite, when they heard a knock at the door. Dan rushed to open the door.

Two distinguished men swept into the room. The taller one reached across the desk to shake his father's hand, "I know you're expecting us. I'm A.J. Lawrence and this is Louis Sohns, Esq. On behalf of Vancouver, welcome to the Territory!" L. Jay motioned for them to sit in the two guest chairs facing the desk. Lawrence continued, "We know your time is valuable, so we'll get right to the point. It's imperative that we move the executive offices to Vancouver."

Sohns broke in, as if on cue, "We can provide far more appropriate facilities for the government. A Vancouver capitol would not have narrow stairs and a cramped office for the governor of this great territory." Sohn spoke with an accent. Later, Dan learned that Sohn grew up in Germany and fled to America as a young man.

Lawrence added, "You are from Illinois and must remember how President Lincoln, as a legislator, got the Illinois state capitol moved from Vandalia to Springfield...."

"I remember very well. My father was a state legislator when Mr. Lincoln and his long nine cohorts got that done." L. Jay replied.

"Governor, you are a leader like Lincoln. Your time should not be wasted in a dump like this!" Sohns added. The Vancouver men explained their plan. Dan got bored with their sales pitch and poked through law books on the shelf near him. He looked up when he heard his father's chair scrape the wooden floor.

"Gentlemen, thank you for coming. I will give your viewpoint fair consideration."

"Governor," Lawrence warned, "we have only a few months before the legislature convenes. This is an urgent issue!"

L. Jay shook their hands, "I will give the issue careful thought. And I know that **wherever** the legislature convenes, we will act on the urgent issues before the territory and the country. We are in the midst of a great war. The resources of every state and territory must help fund the Union cause. Right now, putting down the southern rebellion is more important than moving the capitol south!" The meeting ended. Lawrence and Sohns left.

Dan often came to the governor's office after school. He observed his father's growing agitation and wondered, 'Why isn't he happy?'

One night, Elizabeth scolded her husband, "You are burning the midnight oil too many nights!"

L. Jay thundered, "My work is too important! This is what I've always wanted!" Dan fled to the pantry. He hunkered down by the narrow window and read another Aesop's fable: *A Lesson for Fools* told the story of a crow and a fox. The crow sat high in a tree, proudly holding a piece of stolen meat in its' beak. The fox said, "You are beautiful and ought to be the king of all the birds, if only you had a voice."

The crow wanted to prove he had a voice and opened his mouth and croaked loudly. Of course, he dropped the meat and the fox snapped it up saying, "If you added brains to all your other qualifications, you could be an ideal king."

Dan closed the book and leaned back against a sack of potatoes, thinking, 'My dad is like that crow, He's a governor who wants to be a king.' Just then, his mother called out, "Daniel Braxton, time for bed." When he walked by, she said softly, "Your father is just overly tired, the long trip and all these new responsibilities."

Dan wanted to say, 'We all made the same long trip!', but thought better of it.

In the coming weeks, he learned that if he didn't interrupt his father, he could tag along as the governor went about his duties. Dan perched on a side bench in the office and thumbed through law books. Often, he listened to the conversations between his father, lawmakers, judges or whoever had a bone to pick or a favor to curry.

After Thanksgiving, L. Jay. became more excitable than usual. Elizabeth explained to the children, "Your father is writing his first State of the Territory speech. It is quite a wonderful honor and also a heavy responsibility." Before going to bed, they watched him. strut through the house belting out lines from the upcoming speech.

One day when his father was gone to a meeting, Dan was alone in the governor's office. He shuffled through papers until he found the speech. He picked it up carefully and imagined himself on the stage in front of the territorial legislature. The thirteen-year-old cleared his throat and began to read,

"Gentlemen…custom requires… a 'speech' on this occasion…I believe there is a bright, a glorious future, for the Territory of Washington. She lies between, and in the thoroughfare of populous and mighty nations; a large part of the world's commerce must ultimately pass over her bosom…." Dan stopped reading aloud when he heard someone in the hallway. He skipped ahead to L. Jay's embellished praise of the territory, "She has the thickest, largest and tallest timber that grows, and is undoubtedly the best lumbering country on earth; and yet she contains many beautiful prairies. Her coal, iron, silver and gold fields… surpass, any yet discovered. Her fertile soil produces apples, pears, plumbs and all berries to perfection."

Reading about the fruit made Dan hungry. He glanced over at his bag on the bench. One of those delicious apples was calling his name. "Danny, Danny." The apple wasn't speaking; it was his brother Johnny knocking on the door. Dan rushed back to the desk and tried to position the papers exactly where they had been, then raced back to his bench before answering, "Johnny, come on in."

Johnny pushed open the door, announcing, "Dad will be here in a minute and he said you had to give me one of the apples. Just because you're the oldest, doesn't mean you get to hog everything." Dan offered him a book.

"I can't eat that. Give me an apple."

Dan took an apple from his bag and rolled it across the plank floor, "An apple-a-day, keeps little brother away."

Governor Turney walked in and caught Johnny climbing out from under the desk, holding up a dusty apple and pointing at Dan, who was pretending to read a book. L. Jay said, "Daniel, your book is upside down. Even you can't read that way. Both of you, get out from under my feet. Go back to the house, I've got to rehearse my speech. Tomorrow, I deliver it. December 19th will be a historic day!" Dan hoped he had put the pages back in the right order.

1862

Governor Turney was pleased with his historic speech. He supported the federal government's direct tax to fund the Civil War and told the territorial legislators, "Both patriotism and pride require us to meet that call promptly." The legislature adopted his recommendation and county auditors began collecting the war tax. 1862 was off to a great start; but a few weeks later it all came crashing down. Turney received word from Washington, D.C. that Abraham Lincoln was appointing a new permanent Territorial Governor and his name was not Leander Jay S. Turney, but William Pickering. Pickering would take over in June.

Elizabeth lamented, "L. Jay, I don't understand!"

He snapped. "My old friend Pickering went behind my back and stole my job!"

Dan asked, "What will we do?"

His father's face turned to stone. "We will stay on! Pickering will become Governor, but he'll have to put up with me as Secretary. Lincoln wouldn't dare take that away from me." But Lincoln did. He appointed Olympia's Elliot Evans to succeed L. Jay S. Turney. "I will fight. I won't give up. Evans may think he's appointed, but he came without the appropriate bond. I refuse to vacate the office! The charges against me are bogus!" Dan had never seen his father so upset. Storming out of the door, L. Jay shook his office keys, "'I have the keys and Evans doesn't have the papers!" Both Dan and Johnny were awed at their father's intensity. Elizabeth was fearful. She had seen L. Jay's plots fail too often. Her fears were justified. On December 6, Turney had to give up the job and his keys; but even then, he continued sending letters signed, "L. Jay S. Turney, Secretary W.T." He ran for U.S. Congress, hoping to get out of Olympia. But where could he go until the election?

Dan overheard his uncle John Knox advise, "L. Jay, Walla Walla is the place to go. There's gold nearby; trade and wealth to be had. You can build a new political base with the Germans and the farmers. There's nothing left for you here in Olympia." Elizabeth protested quietly, but the decision had been made and they were on the road again. Dan looked back and caught a last glimpse of the capitol building. 'I'll miss my special bench and the books.'

CHAPTER THREE

Walla Walla, Washington
1863-1865

It was a hard winter trip, winding south and east through the Cascades. They were awed by Mt. Rainier, towering in the distance. Johnny teased Lucy, "Look at that big mountain. Think how big the bears are there!" She ignored him. Dan worried about what was ahead. 'No doubt, more twist and turns. Life is like this military road twisting through the wilderness.' He reminisced about their simpler life in the prairie land of southern Illinois.

Johnny asked, "Where will we live in Walla Walla?"

"On a farm out at the edge of town," Elizabeth said.

Dan turned to his father, "Are you going to become a farmer?"

"No. I'll be practicing law with attorney Otis Bridges. His law practice is growing and he tells me there will be plenty of work for both of us. You boys can help your mother with chores on the farm."

Dan smirked, "So we get to be the farmers and do the hard work?" His father gave him a stern look. Elizabeth stayed silent. She had grown up on a farm and knew how hard it could be. But she had no idea what was before them. When they bounced up the muddy lane to the cabin, even L. Jay could see that they had been deceived by the letter describing the place. Shaking her head in disbelief, Elizabeth groaned, "This can't be it. It can't be!" But it was.

They struggled to make the best of what they found. The broken front door hung on one hinge. Rats scurried across the kitchen floor into a hole in the wall. Rooms were filled with piles of junk and the house smelled of excrement and mold. That was just the beginning. Outside, they found broken fences and a garden space filled with weeds and more junk.

With her usual determination, Elizabeth told them, "Let's get to work." But it got harder for her as the weeks passed. Dan saw her struggle. Johnny whispered, "It's 'cause the baby is coming," They all worked to expand the garden. L. Jay insisted, "We need a big garden, so we won't go hungry." He went to town every day, but the law practice was starting slowly. In May, Dan, Johnny, Margaret and Fannie met their newborn baby sister Sarah.

Mr. Lightfoot, the neighbor who had helped fix the front door, stopped by and asked the boys if they'd like to go hunting. Dan said, "I'd like to learn to shoot a gun." He was tired of digging weeds and chopping wood.

Lightfoot said, "Come on, I'll show you." They walked to the woods back of his place. Dan helped set up a row of tin cans on a big pine log. After a lesson on gun safety, Daniel got his chance to shoot. His first shot hit the log. But his second try sent a can flying. He hit the third and fourth cans. "Dan, you have a good eye and a steady hand. Keep shooting like that and we'll run out of cans and bullets." By the end of the summer, Dan knew he liked shooting better than farming. Hunting became a hobby.

During the winter, the Turneys barely scratched by. Thanks to their big garden and the wild game that Dan shot, they never went hungry. L. Jay's law practice was still not living up to his expectations and he was badly beaten in his run for Congress. "I need a fresh start!" Elizabeth agreed. L. Jay wrote a batch of inquiry letters. Dan helped by copying letters for his dad to sign.

Like most northerners, they celebrated Robert E. Lee's surrender to U.S. Grant on April 9, 1865. The war was over. They were shocked, less than a week later, when President Abraham Lincoln was assassinated. Dan thought about the time he'd met Lincoln back in Illinois. L. Jay pondered his own complex history with Abe, "He selected me and then rejected me." He felt a bitter, tearless grief. Weeks of waiting, fed his dissatisfaction.

L. Jay eagerly ripped open a letter from Salem, Oregon. It was an offer to run a big hotel. "The war is over and they want to expand. There's money to be made!" L. Jay said, "Daniel, what do you think?" Not waiting for an answer, he voiced his own thoughts, "Salem is a political town and nobody knows the political crowd better than I do. I can charm them, house them, feed them and get rich. We'll be across from the courthouse, close to the capitol, right back in the center of things! We can live in a grand hotel instead of this decrepit cabin."

That idea was music to Elizabeth's ears, "When do we pack?" Everyone was ready to say goodbye to Walla Walla.

Dan asked his father, "What about schools in Salem?"

L. Jay said, "That's covered. There's a great school nearby called Wallamet University. I bet they have more books than we had in Olympia. Oregon is already a state."

"Is Salem the capital?" ten-year-old Margaret asked.

"Of course," Johnny scolded, "Don't you know your state capitals yet?"

Margaret stuck out her tongue, making sure her father didn't see.

But L. Jay wasn't looking. His mind was in Oregon, his new home and a new claim to fame. "Salem, here we come!"

CHAPTER FOUR

Salem, Oregon
Fall of 1865

"Salem, at last!" the Turney's cried out as they reached the edge of town. They got directions and headed for State Street. Dan saw it first, "There it is. The Bennett House!" Their eyes drank in the massive two-story building. "Look at those balconies," Johnny said. "It looks like a steam boat." L. Jay agreed, "You're right, son. This hotel was designed by Charles Bennett, a steamboat man." Dan hoped their rooms would be on the second floor. He'd never lived anyplace with a balcony.

When they pulled up to the hitching rails, Dan and Johnny were ready to race to the office. "Boys, hold your horses!" L. Jay scolded. "I need to get us checked in." An hour later, they were in two adjoining rooms. "This will do for tonight," L. Jay said. "Tomorrow I have arrangements to make, papers to sign and a bank to visit." "

After breakfast, L. Jay asked Elizabeth to go with him to meet with Bennett's current owner. "Yes," she said, "but please do not to sign any papers until we see what we're getting into, in the light of day. We don't want another pig in a poke." She had already noticed things in their two rooms that needed work.

"You're right," He said. "I'll go to the office and get a master key, so we can tour the whole place before we meet with the owner." Five minutes later, he returned waving a set of keys. "Why don't we have Dan and Johnny help us with our inspection tour?"

"Two more sets of eyes could help. Margaret can look after Fran and Sarah," Elizabeth added.

It took them until noon to examine every room, most of which were empty. Dan was their scribe and recorded everything that needed fixing, room-by-room. It was a long list. They checked on the girls and headed back to the office, resolved not to sign any papers unless the hotel was fixed up. The owner was irritated by their demands and seemed ready to throw them out. L. Jay countered, "We're offering you a chance to restore the dignity and profitability of this property. How many former governors are making you offers?" The owner shrugged. L. Jay leaned in, "Spruce her up and we'll lease her and you will turn a profit again, or we can walk out and you can keep losing money."

An hour later, Leander Jay S. Turney signed an agreement to lease the Bennett House for two years, subject to the improvements listed in Dan's handwriting. "I expect you, sir, to make immediate arrangements to fix up the Bennett. I am no carpenter." Then he warned, "But I am a lawyer." He waved his copy of the contract. "Good to do business with you."

Afterwards, Elizabeth chided, "Was it wise to threaten him?"

"Elizabeth, sometimes a man just has to lay his cards on the table!"

The months that followed were a blur. Dan enrolled at Wallamet University and the children, except Sarah started school. L. Jay swapped yarns with locals and began connecting with Oregon politicians. The family staked out four restored rooms on the second floor with a balcony as their living quarters. One room had a dining table, reading chairs and a make-shift book case. Dan studied there when he wasn't in classes. His love of books was rekindled and his love of guns faded. His nightly routine included reading stories to six-year-old Fran, who loved books. "Dan, read me another one of Aesop's stories."

"Here's one of my favorites," Dan said. "The tortoise and the hare."

She wriggled with happiness. "I love the turtle and the rabbit."

"Do you want to change the names, or do you want me to read?"

"You can read. I like your voice," Fran said.

"A tortoise and a hare started a dispute about which of them was swifter and they made an appointment to settle the matter. The hare had such confidence in its natural speed that it did not trouble about the race but lay down by the wayside and went to sleep. The tortoise acutely conscious of its slow movements, padded along without ever stopping until it passed the sleeping hare and won the race."

"Slow, but sure, wins the race! Read me another one."

He hugged her, "Not tonight. You pad off to bed like a good tortoise. I have to get back to my big books." She waved at him, but he was already into his U.S. History book.

He'd only read a page when L. Jay interrupted, "Dan, would you take a look at this hotel advertisement I'm writing for the newspaper?"

"Sure," Dan sighed. His dad's smudges and cross-outs were hard to decipher, but with a second reading, he understood them. "BENNETT HOUSE, Salem, Oregon. L. Jay S. Turney, having leased the above hotel, is prepared to accommodate the traveling public, and ONE HUNDRED regular boarders, in as good a style as any house on the coast. He has determined to make the 'Bennett'…better than any public house in Salem…." Dan jumped ahead to a paragraph about 'Charlie', "…the best cook in Salem, and one of the best in the whole country…." His dad could slather it on.

"What do you think?" L. Jay asked.

"Since you're selling Charlies' good food, not 'clap-trap, pomp and show', why don't you headline 'GOOD GRUB AND PLENTY OF IT at the Bennett House….'etc."

"That's a great line!" L. Jay said as he scribbled down Dan's idea. "Those classes at Wallamet are making you smarter.

"Might be. But I started out with a heap of smarts from my Pappy!"

L. Jay smiled and Dan opened his book again.

1866

Dan studied his way through May. School agreed with him. L. Jay's Bennett House plans were taking shape. Elizabeth's shape changed as she prepared to give birth to her eighth child. Leander L. was born into a busy household. When Dan finished his accounting class at Wallamet, his father drafted him to help with the Bennett House books. From his new desk down the hall from the bar, Dan overheard snatches of conversations about politics, business, religion and family woes. He called it 'saloon talk'. The louder versions were usually fueled by alcohol. Dan was learning that drinking seldom improved a man. One afternoon he was adding a column of figures when a boozed-up man barged into the office, knocked over a stack of papers and mumbled, "Sorry, I thought this was the door to the outhouse."

"Two doors down the hall," Dan said curtly.

That night, during their reading time, he told Fran about the encounter with the drunk.

She asked. "Is drinking too much liquor always bad for men?"

"Seems to be."

"Then why does daddy sell it?" she asked.

Dan was silenced. "I suppose he thinks he has to." But her question troubled him as he watched drinkers turn into drunks. Fran's questions were not easily ignored.

The Turneys could not ignore Sarah's cries that night. She struggled to breathe, coughed and choked. Within a couple of hours, Fran was imitating her sick sister. Dan felt helpless watching them gasp for air. Their coughs sounded like dogs barking. He'd heard stories of a rash of sickness among children in Salem. They called it the croup or diphtheria. The family was relieved when Salem's Dr. Cummings came to see the girls. After examining them, he told Elizabeth, "Give them a tablespoon of this compound four times a day with honey tea. And wrap their throats with warm compresses. That should help." She followed the doctor's directions, but the girls got worse. Choking, they croaked, "Mommy, we can't breathe!" Elizabeth clutched baby Leander to her breast and cried out, "Dan, run downstairs and tell your father to get the doctor back here right now!"

Dan rushed downstairs and told his father about the girls.

L. Jay ordered, "Go get Dr. Cummings!"

"Where does he live?" Dan asked.

"Four blocks over on Liberty Street; big house with a double-decker porch...."

Dan almost knocked over two customers as he raced to the street. He was winded when he reached the doctor's house. He pounded on the door. It finally opened and the sleepy-eyed doctor greeted him. "Dr. Cummings, come help us. My sisters can't breathe!"

"At the Bennett House?" he asked. "Let me get my medical bag."

They ran together, retracing Dan's steps until they reached the downtown boardwalk. Their feet drummed on the planking. Both turned when they heard a curse and the crack of a whip. A runaway carriage careened onto the boardwalk and crashed into Dr. Cummings and Dan. The carriage wheels crushed the doctor's neck and left him writhing in agony. Dan got to his knees and saw the face looming above him from the buggy. The driver was the drunk who had staggered into Dan's office. Daniel crawled to the doctor, who had stopped moving. "Doc, Doc!" The carriage lurched back to the street. A whiskey bottle bounced out and shattered. Dan struggled to his feet, crying out, "Help! Help!" A passerby hurried to assist. He felt for the doctor's pulse, then shook his head. "He's gone!"

"We've got to find another doctor!" Dan was frantic. Eventually, one of L. Jay's regulars gave Dan a ride to the house of Salem's other doctor. They rushed back to the Bennett House. Elizabeth met them, "You are too late for Sarah. She stopped breathing. She's gone!" Elizabeth would have collapsed, but L. Jay wrapped his arms around her.

"Where's the sister?" the doctor asked.

"Fran is in there," L. Jay pointed.

The doctor rushed to Fran's side. He urgently examined her. She was writhing and gasping for breath. "Get me water and towels!" the doctor ordered. Daniel's heart stopped when the doctor took his scalpel out of his bag and plunged it into Fran's trachea. It was a desperate, last-ditch effort to save her. But it was too late. Fran died. Dan collapsed into a chair and sobbed. When he closed his eyes, all he could see were Fran's pleading eyes.

The crowd on State Street parted like the Red Sea when the dark figure appeared. The grim reaper singled out the fleeing children and swung his bloody scythe. Heads, arms and legs flew into a growing pile of mutilated bodies. Death, cruel death! The reaper and his bloody blade left a trail of blood and bodies as he burst into the Bennett House charged up the stairs. He crashed through the door, swinging his curved blade and cursing, spattering blood on walls and ceiling. "I come for Fran and Sarah!!" Fran's horrified face filled the black room. The reaper swung his scythe and it morphed into a giant scalpel.

Dan screamed and sat up in bed. The dream ended. No grim reaper was in the room, only his brother Johnny, who had been awaked by his cry. Dan's terrified eyes glowed in the darkness; sweat soaked his bedding and dread filled his heart. Today they were going to bury Fran and Sarah. The nightmare was not real, but their dying was. Dan told Johnny about the dream. Johnny said, "That's scary!"

"It was! Last night I watched Dr. Cummings get killed. I saw the knife go into Fran's neck. I saw her die." Johnny didn't know what to say, so he went back to sleep. Dan pondered his way through the darkness until a frail morning light crept into the room.

A gray December mist shrouded the town. A somber Turney family, deprived of two energetic faces, plodded toward Salem's cemetery following a wagon hauling two small wooden caskets. Six-year-old Fran and Three-year-old Sarah would be buried beside each other. Older sister Margaret formed a poem in her mind, 'Side by side, for eternity to abide.' They walked slowly through the tiny cemetery toward the pile of dirt that marked the grave. L. Jay hugged his sobbing wife as she hugged their baby. The procession reached its dreaded destination. As if on cue, the preacher emerged from the small crowd of onlookers and introduced himself, "Mr. and Mrs. Turney, I'm George Roork, Methodist preacher. I'm sorry to have to meet you on this sad day." Roork tucked his bible under his left arm and greeted each member of the family. He came to Dan and saw the immense grief in the boy's eyes. "May the Lord comfort you!", the preacher said softly.

Rev. Roork invited the crowd to join the Turneys around the caskets. He opened his bible and read about how Jesus invited the little children to come to him. "But his disciples wanted to stop the little ones from coming. Jesus rebuked them and swept the children up in his arms and blessed them. I don't know everything about heaven, but I can imagine Jesus sweeping up the little children, like Fran and Sarah in his arms and welcoming them. He welcomes all who will believe in him. Jesus says in Matthew 11:28, 'Come unto me, all ye that labor and are heavy laden and I will give ye rest.'" Dan felt the words burrow into his mind.

"Come to me, Jesus said. Come when you hurt and I will give you comfort. Come to me when you are broken and I will make you whole. Come to me when you face death and I will give you resurrection. Jesus has gone on ahead of us and is preparing us a house, not made with hands, eternal in the heavens." As Roork spoke, the sun broke through the clouds. The preacher led them in prayer before the caskets were lowered into the ground. Dan took his turn pushing a shovel full of dirt down onto the caskets. When Dan passed his shovel along to brother Johnny, Rev. Roork put a hand on his shoulder, "Don't forget what I said about the Lord's comfort."

Behind them, the local newspaper editor greeted L. Jay, then Elizabeth, "My wife and I sympathize with your loss; we lost our oldest daughter just before we moved out here. I hope this will help," he said, as he handed Leander a folded piece of paper. "I'm going to run it in next week's paper."

Leander unfolded the page and read silently,

"Now, hand in hand, by the crystal sea, The little sisters rove, Where the bright waves beat in ecstasy, And the angels sing of love.

Thus, hand in hand, for a few swift years, To roam, and to watch, and to wait.

Till the rest have passed through the pale of tears, And enter the pearly gate."

That night, Dan's nightmare returned, but the horrifying screams were muted by Rev. Roork's quiet words, "May the Lord comfort you!"

1867

Elizabeth struggled to find comfort and buried her grief deep in winter's work-- keeping her remaining family warm, fed and clean. By the time the daffodils pushed up through the frosty spring earth, the rest of the Turneys were finding a new rhythm of life without Fran and Sarah. Dan replaced his nightly ritual of reading to Fran with time reading from the bible. He went to church every Sunday and most Wednesdays. His faith was coming alive. He soaked it in. His new obsession grew in tandem with his scholarly pursuits at the university. Dan continued working at The Bennett House, but avoided the drinkers. Even the smell of alcohol made him sick and his opinions about drunkenness sharpened. After church, one Sunday, he told Rev Roork, "It's the devil's brew!"

The preacher agreed, quoting Ephesians 5:18, "Be not drunk with wine, but be filled with the spirit."

"Amen, brother!" Dan affirmed in the language of the Methodists.

Roork asked, "How's the Spirit leading you Dan? You have plans after school?"

"Dad thinks I should go into newspaper work. He's already lining up a job for me."

"Where?" the preacher asked.

"Oregon City. He knows D.C. Ireland, publisher of the *Oregon City Enterprise*. Ireland is supposed to be a creative genius. His new weekly paper has four pages, seven columns."

"Four pages, that's a lot of words to write and a lot of type to set!"

"I might look into it. Words are my thing. One classmate calls me *Wallamet's Wordsmith*; another told me that if five small words would do, I would use 50 big ones!"

Roork laughed, "I've used a few big words myself. But a preacher can only use as many words as his people can stomach at one sitting." He got serious, "Daniel, have you ever thought about being a preacher?"

"Grandpa Parish once asked me that same question."

The preacher challenged, "Give it some thought. Pray about it. Go ahead and set some type and write some stories for Mr. Ireland, if he will have you. But, if the Lord wants you to preach, that's what you'll end up doing."

CHAPTER FIVE

Oregon City, Oregon
1868

A year later, Dan got his degree from Wallamet and the newspaper job in Oregon City. He was active in church and often spoke up in his weekly class meeting. The rest of the family wasn't doing as well. The Bennett House was failing. L. Jay lost chef Charlie to a new hotel up in Portland and was desperately trying to scrape up enough money for another year's lease. One evening, the family gathered around the supper table; Daniel, 20, had joined them for the weekend. Margaret, 14, brought in the food from the kitchen, while her mother cared for Leander L., now a fussy toddler. John, 17, was liking school better and told Dan that he preferred the sciences. L. Jay cleared his throat, "I have two announcements for the family. First, I was not nominated to be State's Attorney for Oregon's 3rd Judicial District."

Dan had heard scuttlebutt in the *Enterprise's* newsroom. His father's dramatic return to the courtroom in Walla Walla had sunk his chances. During a trial, Judge James D. Mix called L. Jay Turney names and his father reacted by clubbing the judge with his gold-knobbed cane. Dan knew that kind of behavior was more likely to make him a felon than a State's Attorney.

"My second announcement is more important. It will affect all of us." L. Jay said. He paused, until all were looking toward the head of the table. "Your mother and I have decided to leave Oregon and move back to Illinois."

Johnny and Margaret were shocked and sat in bewildered silence. L. Jay continued with a convoluted explanation of why they needed to leave. Dan, keeper of the Bennett House books, knew the financial failure all too well. Then there were his dad's bad investments in California real estate, which had been lost in a devastating fire. Dan's thoughts turned darker, 'Maybe Judge Mix is going to bring legal charges and dad is escaping to Illinois?' Dan's thought train was derailed by his father's direct question, "What about you, Daniel? Are you coming with us to Illinois?" Everyone, even little Leander, turned and looked his way.

"I'll stay here!" Dan exclaimed. "I just started working with Mr. Ireland and I'm getting the hang of newspaper work." L. Jay nodded. He had published a newspaper in Shawneetown, IL, back when Dan was still in diapers. Like many things in his life, *The Southern Illinois Advocate* had failed. Dan continued, "I also have friends at church and in my class meeting."

Margaret looked puzzled. "I thought you were finished with classes?"

Dan explained, "I was talking about my Methodist church class meetings. We meet in groups of ten or twelve to encourage each other, hold each other accountable. I wouldn't want to be without my class meeting."

"Son, it sounds like you're choosing them over your family?"

"Dad, they are like family to me," Dan retorted.

Elizabeth intervened, "I understand, Dan. I used to be part of class meeting back in Benton."

L. Jay. said, "Elizabeth, we'll be heading back to Illinois and you can see your Pa and Ma again. They are kin. They are our true family!"

Dan scooted back his chair. He felt rebuked and would soon be left behind.

A month later, his Turney family moved back to Illinois; Dan stayed in Oregon with his new Methodist family. Rev. George H. Roork become like an older brother. He listened attentively to Dan's stories about D.C. Ireland teaching him to throw type, lock the lines in place, ink the rollers and print a sheet of paper. It was a complicated, intricate process. Dan told George, "I love books, but I'd rather read them than print them." Roork eventually loaned him every book in his library. Dan read the M.E. Book of Discipline, two books of John Wesley's sermons, a Methodist hymnal and Wesley's commentary on the New Testament.

May 10, 1869

In Early May, Dan was back in Salem walking Main Street with Rev. Roork. Their pace and their debate were brisk. "George, I just want to be clear about what Mr. Wesley said about baptism."

"Dan, he wrote a lot about baptism and always tied it to grace."

"Wesley tied everything to grace, didn't he?"

Roork nodded and pointed to a rail in front of a store, "Grace was Wesley's favorite hitching post." Before Dan could respond, the door to the Western Union office burst open and a man ran into the street waving a telegram shouting, "Done! Done!" Within minutes church bells rang and an excited crowd gathered.

"What's happened?" Roork asked."

"They finished the transcontinental railroad! Bigwigs drove the golden spike at Promontory Summit connecting the Union Pacific and the Central Pacific Rail lines. Sacramento has a direct line to all the way to New York City!"

"Daniel, your folks went back to Illinois a few month's too early. Now they could take the train."

Dan nodded, thinking about his family and his future. He made a fist to hide the ink under his fingernails and said, "I'm not sure I'm cut out to be a newspaper man."

Roork said, "Before you decide, I'd like you to meet a newspaper friend of mine, W.B. Carter, editor of *The Corvallis Gazette.*"

"I've read some of his stuff. Would be glad to meet him."

A couple of months later, Roork escorted Dan into the newspaper office and introduced him to Carter. They hit it off, right away. Carter mesmerized Dan with his passion about prohibition, "I have no malice or hatred against any individual, but I loathe and abhor the liquor business! It's the devil's own engine of war; the battering ram…by which he seeks to break down religion and morality, and overturn the foundations of free government. The harlot, the debauchee, the ignorant and abandoned on earth are his cohorts and allies…."

"I don't drink!" Dan exclaimed.

"Good for you, Daniel. Our friend George tells me you intend to become a Methodist preacher and you're already a licensed Exhorter. That so?"

"Yes, sir! Dallas Circuit since January 17."

"Going to serve the Lord and fight Demon Rum?"

"Those two go together, don't they?" Dan responded. "I've been talking with Rev. Roork about going back to Illinois to preach."

"Not enough sinners out here?" Carter teased.

"Plenty, I reckon, but Rev. Roork and his brother can handle them."

Carter asked, "When you going back?"

"Before fall."

"Has brother George, told you about the National Prohibition Convention in Chicago?"

"He has," Dan said.

"Some of us from the Oregon Templars of Temperance are going as delegates. Why don't you join us? The fight for prohibition needs young blood, new leaders."

Dan was all ears. "When?"

"Just three weeks off, on September first. We're taking the Transcontinental Rail Road from Sacramento, California straight to Chicago. We leave two weeks from Saturday. What do you say?" Dan glanced at George Roork, who knew he was about to lose his young disciple.

Roork reached over and grabbed Dan's hand, "We need to pray about this!" He led them to their knees on the hard floor. Ignoring others in the newsroom, Roork prayed. Both Turney and Carter joined in.

With a loud "Amen", Dan leaped to his feet and grabbed Roork in a bear hug, "George, you were right. I have to preach!" He turned to Carter, "But first, I'll join you for that train ride to Chicago!"

"Fantastic! We'll send in your convention registration and order another Union Pacific ticket."

"I've got some letters of my own that need writing," Dan said. "And I better get packing." When he got back to his boarding house room, he realized all he had to pack was one rumpled suit with tell-tale printer's ink stains and a couple of shirts. Mostly he had books, dozens and dozens of books. He stuffed them into an old steamer trunk. He could barely lift it. 'How will I ever get this down the stairs?' With the help of thoughtful strangers, he managed to get his precious cargo to the train station.

Carter greeted him, "Turney, you look plum tuckered out. Can't have our young-blood wearing out before we start! Gentlemen, give him a hand with that trunk." The trio could barely move it to the tracks. "Turney, are you hauling lead and gold back to Illinois?"

"No sir. Just my books, an old suit and two shirts," he answered, brandishing his tiny suitcase."

"'Travel light and you'll travel far', my Pappy used to say," Carter responded. "Here are your tickets, you won't travel far without them. Let me introduce you to one of our companions on this trip, Mr. J.E. Vinton." Vinton and Turney shook hands. Carter added, "We'll meet E.Z.C. Judson in California before we head east." Dan smiled, "Judson, with his E.Z.C. moniker, might be related to my father, L.J.S. Turney." They boarded the train.

CHAPTER SIX

Sacramento to Chicago
August 1869

In Sacramento, they changed trains to head east. E.Z.C. Judson, a bubbling extrovert, pumped Dan's hand. They were seatmates on this leg of the trip. Once settled into his seat, Dan couldn't resist asking, "What does E.Z.C. stand for?"

"Edward, Zane, Carroll."

"Family names?" Dan asked.

"You are right about that! Mr. Turney, do you have any name beside Daniel?"

"Daniel **Braxton!** Braxton is a family name. My grandad Braxton Parish claims we are descended from Carter Braxton, a signer of the Declaration of Independence."

Judson nodded, "I remember Carter from that day in Philadelphia...." Daniel didn't get it, until Judson laughed. "Hey, I wasn't at the signing! I'm not that much older than you are!" Judson entertained Dan with yarn after yarn, tale after tale. Their conversations deepened as the train climbed the long grades up into the mountains. Judson, seated next to the window, was the tour guide. "Look at that cliff!" Dan gasped in wonder. Suddenly, darkness swallowed them. The train burrowed its way into the first of many mountain tunnels. Dan instinctively put his hands over his ears to block the sound until they popped back into the sunshine. Judson refocused his eyes, then tapped on the window. "I recognize that peak, we'll soon be in mountain goat country. My third western novel was set here in Nevada."

Dan interrupted, "You're a writer?"

"Some accuse me of it, but I hide behind my pen name, Ned Buntline. My folks back east would disown me for ruining the family reputation with my wild westerns."

"What do you mean wild westerns?" Dan asked.

"Well, to be honest, I write what the pundits call 'Dime Novels'. I crank the pulps out, five or six a year and make a lot of dimes."

Dan admitted, "I've never heard of dime novels."

"Kid, you've been hanging around with the high-fluting, over-educated, highbrow crowd. That book you're reading tells me you're a classical man!"

"Latin and Greek," Dan said sheepishly.

"No shame there. I had my brush with that pair. But now I write for the common man and to be honest, that's what pays. While I'm in Chicago, I'm going to promote my books and my latest project."

"Project?"

"Yes. I discovered this buffalo hunter and I'm going to sell him big-time!"

Dan was hooked. "Who is he?"

"You haven't heard about him yet, but you will. Name is William Cody. He can ride and shoot with the best. I'm going to promote him as Wild Bill Cody." Judson remembered his manners and said, "Tell me about your father, this Governor Turney character."

"He's had a wild life!" Dan admitted and then told his father's story.

Judson laughed, slapping his knee, "I don't know anyone else who got both hired and fired by Abe Lincoln."

"I met Lincoln once," Dan said. "He came to our house to visit with my father about Illinois politics."

"Well, shake my hand," Judson said. "You met the man I most respected, but never met." They exchanged stories all the way to Cheyanne. Stepping off the train, they had to dodge workers hurrying to load wood to fuel the steam engine. Judson led them to a nearby hotel. "Some of these railroad hotels serve great grub."

Vinton caught up with them, "I'm ready for a hot steak and potatoes."

"They'll offer a fine spread." Judson looked at his pocket watch. "We've got plenty of time. What do you want, Daniel?"

"I'm hankering for some fresh brewed coffee."

"I'll have a cup of that with you! I'm tired of train tea," Carter said.

After the meal, Dan walked back to the train station with Carter. The editor said, "I wanted to brief you about the convention, and I'd like to hear your thoughts about Methodist baptism." Dan was more than willing to share his ideas on baptism, so he traded seats with Vinton and launched into a passionate discourse on baptism.

CHAPTER SEVEN

Chicago
August 30, 1869

The delegation was delayed in Omaha, waiting to catch the ferry to cross the Missouri River. Boarding another train, they sped across Iowa to Illinois. When they reached the outskirts of Chicago, Dan closed his book and exclaimed, "This is the way travel!" He ran his hand across the shiny seat frame. "You can keep your slow, bumpy buggies, I'll take the train!" The train curved its way into Chicago's Great Central Depot. They borrowed a hand cart to move Dan's trunk to busy Michigan Avenue and caught a streetcar to their hotel. The next morning, the four of them walked through Lake Front Park to stretch their legs and get a look at Lake Michigan. They walked north to Madison Street and then over to Farwell Hall. In the lobby, Dan said, "Wow! This is the biggest building I've ever seen!"

Judson said, "It's brand spanking new and seats more than 3,000."

Dan took a deep breath, "It still smells new."

A lively crowd funneled through the doors into the massive hall. Judson led the way toward the front. They claimed four seats on the fifth row. Conversation, laughter and the sounds of chairs being folded down echoed through the hall. Dan didn't know what to expect; he was a newcomer in his home state and a stranger to Chicago.

The meeting was called to order and chair John Russell spoke, "…This Convention… is but a spontaneous expression of the deep and rapidly spreading conviction that it is time for another forward movement in the great temperance reform. People who fear God and regard the social and moral welfare of their fellow men are… beginning to realize the necessity for some stronger and more formal bond of union between those who favor legal prohibition of the liquor traffic. Hence, the object of our meeting is to organize a separate and independent party, advocating among its most important measures, prohibition of the importation, manufacture and sale of all intoxicating drinks."

The crowd burst into applause. Many, including Dan, rose to their feet. Russell motioned for them to be seated. "While we may use great plainness of speech, let all things be done in charity. Moreover, we should all be deeply impressed that even the most highly exalted human wisdom needs Divine illumination. I call upon Rev. Dr. Evarts of this city, to open with prayer." Turney poked Judson and gave him the universal sign to be quiet. Evarts prayed, his booming voice echoing through the hall.

The day was filled with introductions, reports, prayer meetings, resolutions, debates and votes. Some speakers droned on and on, full of themselves. Judson, leaned over to Dan and whispered, "When it's my turn to speak, I will not bore you like that guy just did."

Dan was surprised. "You are giving a speech?"

"Tonight," the novelist replied. When Judson finished his brief and engaging presentation, Dan knew he'd met a master of public speaking. 'I hope I can do half as well in front of a crowd.' They wrapped up the evening with singing. Walking back to their rooms, both Vincent and Carter congratulated Judson on his delivery.

Carter, walking beside Dan, said, "Judson sure can engage an audience! Did you take notes, my young friend?"

"I did. He had them in the palm of his hand, even at the end of a long day!"

Thursday's session started with a hopeful prayer, but went downhill with the reading of a letter from New York's champion of Temperance, E.C. Delevan. He favored Prohibition, but disapproved the organization of a third political party. Murmurs of confusion rippled through the crowd. Delevan's opinion could not be easily dismissed. But the platform committee forged ahead. "...Whereas, the traffic in intoxicating drinks greatly impairs the personal security, personal liberty of large masses of citizens...." Dan's mind wandered back to Oregon and his sisters' graves. He vaguely heard the speaker condemn the inaction of existing political parties.

Debates and amendments followed, but the convention struggled to name itself. Some wanted *Anti-Dram-Shop*. Others wanted *Temperance*. At a late hour, they settled for *The National Prohibition Party*. Other resolutions tried to lay out future plans, including suffrage. "...Protection is equally right, therefore suffrage should be impartial without regard to nationality, color or sex." Dan noted that several women rose to speak on the connection between prohibition and suffrage.

But it was a resolution made by Rev. C.D. Pillsbury that planted seeds in Daniel's mind. Pillsbury warned, "The traffic in intoxicating liquors is the great cause of Sabbath desecration. We recognize the prohibition of liquor traffic as the most promising measure to preserve the sacredness of that holy day." It triggered a memory of one of Rev. Roork's sermons and unleashed an avalanche of ideas in Dan's mind. 'Unholiness leads to unfaithfulness; unfaithfulness leads to drinking; drinking leads to death!'

When the convention adjourned, Dan excused himself from his western colleagues and hurried to the front to find Rev. Pillsbury. "Sir, it's urgent that I talk with you." Back in his room that night, Dan frantically scribbled down ideas about the sabbath, while his group slept. He took a break to see them off to the railroad station. Ideas burned in his mind as he left Chicago to go south to Benton, Illinois, where his grandfather Braxton Parish lived. Dan needed to tap the old preacher's wisdom, before his head exploded.

CHAPTER EIGHT

Benton, IL
1869-1870

The dark sky exploded with thunder and lightning as Dan's train pulled into Benton. He checked his trunk of books at the station, "I'll borrow Grandpa's buggy and come back for them tomorrow." The weary clerk handed him a ticket stub and Dan trudged off into the rain, clutching his suitcase under his arm. He was soaked to his bones by the time he slogged to his grandparent's house. He still recognized the tiny cottage.

But his grandfather barely recognized him. "Daniel, is that you?" Braxton Parish, in his night clothes, hugged Daniel Braxton. "Oh, Danny, it's been so long. Eight years too long! Come on in and close that door. We're both wet enough. Let me get you some dry duds. You can change in the pantry."

Dan stepped out of the pantry and his grandfather handed him a hot cup of tea. They sat at the old table, sipped tea and talked in whispers. "Your grandma hasn't been well for weeks and needs her sleep." Dan, longed to unload his ideas on the old preacher, but it wasn't the right time. They needed to sleep. Dan scrunched up on the cot the Parishes had set up for him in an empty corner. Braxton carefully crawled back in bed with his wife Margaret.

Dan woke to the smell of brewing coffee. His grandfather said, "Danny, your clothes have dried and I put them next to the table. Grandma will be out in a jiffy."

Dan got dressed just as Margaret hobbled into the room. She steadied herself with a knobby wooden cane. "Danny, Danny! It is so good to see you all growed up!" He gave her a gentle hug. She gripped him ferociously, dropping her cane in the process. He picked it up and helped her to the table.

The three talked and drank coffee. Dan had read about 'holy moments' in one of Roork's books and knew this was such a time. "Your letters were a Godsend," Margaret said, squeezing his hand. "We were so saddened when your sisters died. Your family had so many troubles out west." She wiped a tear from her eye. Dan could see the eighty years of pioneer life etched into her face. Margaret composed herself and managed a smile, "But we are so happy God has called you to the ministry."

Braxton added, "Even as a young boy, I could see the preacher in you!"

"Grandpa, you give me a lot to live up to!"

"You'll serve the Lord well! I saw that in your letters." Braxton answered.

"Thanks Grandpa. I could use your help in figuring out how to get into the Methodist Episcopal Church, here in Illinois. I also have some big ideas I need to run by you."

"We'll talk when you get back from the depot with your precious trunk. I'd like to see the books you've collected."

"Can you help me hitch up your buggy?"

Braxton stood, "Let's do it right now. Margaret, you go rest up. I'll be right back to clean up the breakfast dishes."

Dan was relieved to find that his book trunk was bone dry. The train agent helped him load the books in the carriage. When they unloaded it, Daniel discovered his grandfather still had lots of strength in his lean frame. When they opened the trunk, the old preacher was like a kid in a candy shop. "Look at these books." He waved a thin old volume, "I've read this one. Here's your Greek New Testament. I never had the schoolin' to learn Greek."

"Wallamet taught me well, but I'm still learning."

"Me, too!" the old man admitted.

That afternoon, after Margaret was back in bed for her nap, Dan asked, "Can we talk about what's been troubling me?"

Braxton poured him another cup of coffee. "What's on your mind?"

Dan pulled out a fistful of crumpled papers, filled with scribbled notes, arrows and diagrams. "It's about the Sabbath, Grandpa. A speaker at the Convention set a fire in my head that I can't put out."

"Careful, Dan. Fire warms, but can also burn."

"My Sabbath ideas are a good fire. The original Edenic Sabbath was a day of rest. It was to commemorate creation. But that creation was marred by the fall of man. The New Creation, that God the Savior is forming out of the ruins of the old, is far the greater and more illustrious creation of the two. Its glory is indescribable. It is magnificent beyond description. Both creations are the work of Christ. 'For by him were all things created, that are in heaven, and that are in earth, visible and invisible, whether there be thrones or dominions, or principalities, or powers: all things were created by him and for him (Col. 1:16).' And by his precious blood and mighty power sinners are redeemed by God."

The old preacher struggled to keep up. "Slow down, son! Your fire is burning too fast for me."

"Sorry," Dan said. He took a sip of his coffee and thumbed through his notes. "What I'm trying to say is that our Christian Sabbath doesn't just commemorate creation and command us to rest from our work."

"What else, then?" Braxton asked.

"The resurrection! The first day of the week was the day of joy to the disciples of our Savior. Then their hopes were revived; their fears were scattered; their griefs were terminated; their sorrows at an end. Then their joy was full, and their hearts were happy. The day of his resurrection was the day of their triumph!"

"Preach it!" Braxton said, with new fire in his old eyes. "You need to take that on the road for folks to hear. Or maybe, write a book!"

His grandfather's enthusiasm stoked Daniel's fire. "Yes, that's what I'll do. I'll write the book and I'll dedicate it to you!"

Braxton gripped his arm, "Don't get ahead of yourself. It'll take a lot of work to change your scribbles into a book, worthy of resting in the Turney Book Trunk over there."

"Then, I better get started!" Dan said.

"We've got paper and ink behind you in the hutch. You write your Sabbath book; I'll write your folks up in Effingham to let them know you got here, all wet, but fired-up." Dan wrote and rewrote as falling leaves were covered with falling snow. He helped his grandparents with chores, chopped firewood and fed the horse. Braxton coached Dan on how to get into the Methodist Episcopal ministry and introduced him to pastors in the area.

"Grandpa, do you know everyone in southern Illinois?"

Margaret bragged, "At least everyone in Franklin and Williamson Counties!"

Braxton shrugged. "I know all the folks at Benton Methodist. My friend Alex McCreery reminded me on Sunday that we started our church twenty years ago."

"It's been that long?" Margaret said.

"Yes, it has. They want to have a twenty-year wingding in the spring and asked me to preach. I turned them down."

"Why? Braxton, you never refuse to preach."

"I had a reason. I told them I'd rather they asked my grandson Daniel Braxton Turney to preach. It's well and good to reminisce about the past, but better to hear a voice from the future."

Dan was stunned. Braxton said, "It's time Dan. You can start preaching where I finished up. I'm passing the torch. You've got to carry the fire!"

"I would be honored, Grandpa! But will they ask me?"

"Don't you worry, none. I already told them you are going to do it."

Dan quickly shifted his attention from his Sabbath book to his Benton sermon. He almost jumped out of his chair when Braxton rushed into the room, waving a letter. "Elizabeth and Leander are moving to Benton! They bought the house next door."

"When?" Dan and Margaret asked in unison.

"In two weeks!"

"They'll be here in time for the big celebration and for Danny's first sermon!" Margaret exclaimed. Dan wondered how his father would react to being compelled to go to church. L. Jay S. Turney considered himself a reprobate. 'I better make my sermon a good one,' Dan thought. Margaret wept in gladness. Her daughter Elizabeth would live next door. Visits had been few and far between, even in the year since the Turneys moved back to Illinois.

The days flew by and before he knew it, his family was in Benton and Dan was carrying his bible down the aisle of the Methodist Episcopal church. His parents and siblings were seated in the festive crowd.

People applauded when Braxton Parish stood to introduce Dan. Braxton waved off their affection, "We're here this afternoon to praise the Lord and thank him for twenty years of ministry in this town. Benton M.E. Church welcomes Mt. Vernon district Presiding Elder B.R. Pierce. It is my honor to introduce our preacher for the day, my grandson Daniel Braxton Turney. By the way, he was just two years old when the church started."

Dan stood, but waited for his grandfather to sit before stepping behind the pulpit. He opened his bible. "Hear ye the word of the Lord from Revelation 22:7. 'Behold, I come quickly: blessed is he that keepeth the sayings of the prophecy of this book.' It is sometimes difficult for the preacher to select a proper text for a sermon. Today's text, contains a promise: 'Behold, I come quickly.' God counts not as we count. 'One day with him is as a thousand years, and a thousand years as one day.' But he will not tarry. When the last prophecy has been accomplished, he will come suddenly."

Dan let his words sink in. "But the text is not confined to a promise; it contains a blessing: 'Blessed is he that keepeth the sayings of this book.' Anyone can obtain this blessing. A personal compliance is all that is demanded of you. You see the way, walk in it. I believe the Bible. Its words are true. It reveals the way of salvation. They are unalterable, and will never be changed. No other revelations from our Creator need to be expected. None others are promised.

Our Maker can read our hearts. He knows our inclination to disobey and our inclination for new revelations of our own fabrication. Some hanker after strong delusions. No need of delusion! There is no necessity for us to go astray. Temptations beset us. The Lord can deliver us out of them. As we allow our hearts to be shaped by his written word, we will bear the imprint of his law. Partakers of the Divine nature on earth may reach the mansion of glory in heaven. The witness of the Spirit is the proof of the remission of sins and the proof that you are a member of his family. You have passed from death unto life. We are buried with him, by baptism, into death, that, like Christ was raised from the dead, so we also should walk in newness of life. God sustains his worshipers by the regeneration and renewing of the Holy Spirit."

Dan avoided looking at his father, as he continued, "Every person here must be called into court. You and I will see Jesus transformed from the Lamb who takes our sins, into the Lion who punishes the sinners. The Lamb of God is also the Lion of the tribe of Judah. The advocate becomes the judge. The law will take its course and its penalties will be enforced by him in whom the fulness of the Godhead dwells bodily. Escape from his wrath! You cannot. Produce your blood-signed pardon! Show the seal of your redemption! You cannot, cannot, cannot!!! It is the hour of midnight with you. Your lamp is going out for want of oil. You cannot buy; the stores are closed."

His voice rose, "Turn ye! Christ knocks at the door today; death may violently force open that door tomorrow- and woe be to you if Christ our advocate be not found within. Only through the merit of Jesus Christ, not through what you have done or can do, can you be accounted righteous before God, so as to be saved by grace. Jesus, who arose from the dead after his crucifixion, calls upon you to repent, believe, obey. Prepare for the visitor 'Death!' If we are well prepared for his visit, his appearance will not strike us with terror; but if we are dreading his approach, his coming will be terrible. His eyes flash fiery glances; his features are odious and repulsive; from his lips drip the black surges of separation, and his sword is wet with blood to its very hilt. What will be your hope in death, when you are without hope in life? God pity you!

There will come a time when death will be cut off and the dead shall be raised- some in glory, some to shame. We learn this in the Bible. What a glorious time that will be! Unless saved in Christ, we are in danger of death and hell. This is true. Words to justify or to condemn us. 'Behold! I come quickly; blessed is he that keepeth the sayings of the prophecy of this book.'"

After the festivities, well-wishers greeted Dan. He met three Braxtons, all named after his grandfather, "Our family looks up to Father Parish," one said. Just then Dan saw his own father awkwardly waiting. "Daniel B., those were fine words, fine indeed." As an afterthought, L. Jay added, "Even for a preacher. You have a way with words, son. I still think you could be an exceptional writer."

"I *am* a writer, dad! My book is almost finished. I've sent letters of inquiry to some publishers, one in Chicago."

"Good for you! Maybe you can both write and preach?" L Jay Turney stepped aside to make room for the crush of church people waiting to greet Dan.

After the chicken dinner, Dan met with Presiding Elder B.R. Pierce. Pierce reminded him of his father-- stern and bossy, "Tell me about your conversion? When did you get your call to ministry? Are you willing to go where you are sent? Why did you come back to Illinois? Do you have a copy of your Oregon Exhorter's License?" The questions kept coming. Dan, exhausted after his first sermon, disliked being grilled like a pig on a spit. Back in Oregon, he'd seen Presiding Elders keep pastors tightly reined in. Dan didn't want a bit in his mouth.

The next day, he expressed his feelings to his grandpa. Parish said, "Rev. Pierce is just fulfilling his calling. His job is to guide preachers. The M.E. Church gives him that authority. Preachers submit to that leadership."

"I don't like feeling a bit in my mouth. I don't want to be jerked around. I don't know about submitting?"

"Dan, we submit to leaders because we submit to Christ. Presiding Elders represent Christ and take on the mantel of leadership. Why don't you work on your Sabbath Book and give the bit in your mouth a rest?"

"Thanks Grandpa. I'll do that."

"I need to go give Grandma some care, she tires out so easily."

Dan apologized, "Hope my preaching yesterday wasn't too much for her?"

"Don't worry Danny. Your being here has meant a lot to her and you've been a big help. We'll miss you when you move in with Elizabeth and your family next week." Seeing the look in Dan's face, he added, "Now don't mope, we'll still be right next door. Your cousin Robert is moving in to help us. You remember that Robert's father died the summer your family headed west?"

"That must have been a hard time for you and grandma?" Dan said.

"It was. We felt like we lost a son and a daughter the same week. Robert's mother has remarried and he needs a place to live. Margaret and I need extra help." Braxton looked like he could cry. "She's failing, Danny. And I'm not what I used to be." Dan walked around the table and gave his grandpa a hug. Braxton looked up, "Thanks. Words are important, but sometimes folks just need a hug."

"You're right, but I've always been better at words than hugs." He walked next door to the new Turney house and was warmly greeted by brother Johnny.

"Welcome home, big brother. At least it will be a short move. You'll have to sleep with little Leander, I've got my own bed."

"Hear you've got a job, too!" Dan said.

"I'm a blacksmith for now. But still want to be a doctor."

"That would mean more schooling!"

"You survived it didn't you? I've read a caboodle of books since Oregon. I even perused some of dad's law books!" John responded.

"You'd be welcome to read some of mine!"

John asked, "How about that book you are supposedly writing?"

"It's not a delusion," Dan retorted. "I just got an acceptance letter from a Chicago book company!"

"Didn't mean to doubt you Dan! If anybody knows enough words to create a book, it would be you. I remember a few words from your famous first sermon: compliance, unalterable, remission, regeneration and redemption. I liked your description of death. When are you preaching again?"

Dan said, "In September I'll find out if the M.E.'s want me and then they'll tell me where they want me to go."

"Here in Illinois?"

"Southern half of the state."

"September will be here soon enough," John replied. "I'm looking into medical schools. Grandpa Turney got his medical training by apprenticing in Kentucky, but many doctors today go the schooling route."

"Wish you the best. At least we'll be able to write each other."

John said, "If you can read my scribblin'!"

Two days later, Dan sat at the table with his mother. Elizabeth said, "I'm worried about my mom. She seems to be getting weaker."

"I've seen that too! Yesterday, Grandma was still in bed at noon. She didn't even have her windows open."

"That's not like her. She always liked feeling the breeze on her face."

Dan said, "That's not right. It's late June, Mom."

"I know...." She was interrupted by a knock.

Tom Dillon, a neighbor, was at the door. "Mrs. Turney, today I'm wearing my census-taker hat, Can I get your family information now?"

Elizabeth said, "Of course, Tom. Come on in. My husband and one son are not here, but we'll give you our family information." He stepped in, holding a stack of forms.

"Looks like you're finishing up?" Dan said.

"Yes I am. I learned how to do census work from Father Parish. Back in '60, I tagged along. I was trained by the best!"

Dan's teen-aged sister Margaret waltzed into the room, "Do I get to be in the census?"

"Everybody counts in the 1870 census," Dillon replied as he began filling out the form. They decided that Johnny should be listed as a blacksmith, since he hadn't gone to medical school yet. Dan asked to be listed as 'preacher', even though he had only one sermon under his belt. Elizabeth answered for L.J.S., who was up in Mt. Vernon drumming up new law clients. When he finished, the census-taker told Dan, "May the Lord bless your preaching!"

"I'll need the Lord's blessing and more," Dan replied.

Margaret asked, "What could be more than God's blessing?"

"The blessing of the Methodist Episcopal Church."

CHAPTER NINE

Lebanon, Woodburn and Metropolis
Fall 1870

Three months later, Daniel B. Turney waited nervously for that blessing. He sat in the Lebanon M.E. church with seven other candidates for the Methodist ministry. The air was thick with humidity and anxiety. Dan was squeezed between Joseph Van Cleve and William Mabry. He wondered how they could be so calm. Dan was clear about his call to preach, but church elders had to bless that calling. If they voted to confirm him, he would be admitted on trial. If not, he would be out on his ear. While they waited, Mabry said, "Once we make it through the trial period, we become elders; official, bona fide, approved Methodist Episcopal preachers."

When the door opened, all eight turned as if choreographed, and watched Presiding Elder B.R. Pierce scan the crowd. He motioned to Dan. Van Cleve stepped into the aisle to let him pass. Dan's heart pounded, but he stood straight and walked tall. Elder Pierce extended his hand, "D.B. Turney, congratulations. You've been approved as a ministerial candidate."

"Thank you, sir!"

"You will also receive an appointment to preach." Dan glanced back to his colleagues on the pew and smiled. Pierce continued, "This is only the first step toward ordination."

Daniel Braxton Turney was appointed to the Methodist Episcopal church in Woodburn, a village in Macoupin County, north of St. Louis. He only had a few days to pack. Once at Woodburn, he settled quickly into the rhythm of preparing and delivering weekly sermons. He tried to get the hang of the other parts of ministry, but the town felt tight-knit and unwelcoming. He wrote grandpa Parish, "This place sure doesn't feel like Benton or Fairfield. Everyone in the county is up in arms about the new courthouse. It is as big as the state capitol building in Springfield and has put the county eight-hundred-thousand dollars in debt. This is a prideful place. My church folks are not much better; they are downright haughty about the new bell they have in the church belfry. They use any excuse to ring it—weddings, funerals and even meetings. An old-timer named R.R. Wood told me, *Woodburn is a good place to emigrate from.* Sorry to be such a whiner, but this place is not bringing out the best in me."

1871

When Daniel got his official Methodist Preachers' License on July 29, he learned that he would be moved to a new church in September. 'Grandpa warned me that most M.E. preachers stay for only a year or two. I'll be relieved to leave Woodburn.'

In September, Dan hopped a train, eager to get to the M.E. church Conference down in Cairo. You couldn't go further south and still be in Illinois. He was almost a week early, so he had time to burn. Dan hoofed it to the Cairo M.E. church. He'd met the pastor, Fred Thompson, last year and looked forward to talking with him again, He found Thompson in his office, just off the sanctuary.

"Daniel Turney, good to see you again." Thompson said warmly. He moved a stack of books from a chair and invited Dan to sit. "Do you go by Daniel or do you prefer Dan?

"Dan is fine!"

"Tell me about your first year. You are up in Woodburn, aren't you?"

"I am. But I expect the Bishop to move me this week. To be honest, I hope he does." Thompson was easy to talk with. He was just a few years older than Dan and was warm and engaging. "Fred, where'd you serve before Cairo?"

"Shawneetown."

Dan almost jumped out of his chair. "Shawneetown! That's where I was born."

Thompson said, "Folks like to say that good things come out of Shawneetown! Speaking of good things, I hear that you are writing a book about the Sabbath."

"I submitted my manuscript to a Chicago publisher. I expect to hear from them any day now." They talked about Dan's book and his ideas about the Christian Sabbath.

"Dan, our county has been all stirred up by folks attacking our Methodist ways of baptizing, making us the butt of ridicule. Let me show you." He pulled a newspaper clipping from a stack on his desk and handed it to Dan. "This kind of talk gets my dander up, but I don't know how to argue with it!"

Dan quickly read the article signed by *Eusebius*. He jumped up and waved the clipping at Thompson, "That's pure doggerel! Hogwash! He can't get away with saying this. I want to fire off an answer. Fred, can I borrow your desk, a pen and paper?"

"Help yourself. I've got to run home for a minute to check with my wife Mollie."

Before the office door closed, Dan was scratching out an inspired answer. When Thompson returned, Dan handed him the finished document, "Careful, the ink is still wet."

"Whew! Dan you got him! His folly will be splattered all over Cairo. Let's take this right over to *The Cairo Bulletin's* editorial office. When we get back, Mollie will have a fine lunch spread out for us."

Dan and Fred had many more conversations before Annual Conference met at Fred's church. As they entered the sanctuary, Dan said, "Thanks to you, I feel a lot more comfortable about being on trial than I did last year." Fred played host and Dan sat with the same seven preachers he was with last year. He watched as each of the others were continued and their character passed. When Dan's turn came, his case was reported, but then 'laid over'. He asked Thompson what that meant.

"Tabled. Undecided. Sorry Dan." On the second day, Dan's case was again 'laid over.' Dan feared rejection. On the last day of Conference, at the last possible moment, one of the presiding elders said, "I can put D.B. Turney to good use!" The conference voted to approve him with stomping of feet and clapping of hands. Dan was encouraged and listened attentively as the Bishop Simpson read, "Daniel B. Turney will be assigned to the Metropolis Circuit." He was excited to be in the county east of Cairo. Thompson joked, "You can almost see Cairo from Metropolis." Later, Dan discovered he would serve three small churches strung together in a preaching circuit.

Before leaving Conference, Dan wrote his grandpa Parish, "Did you ever serve a circuit of churches? I'll preach twice Sunday mornings and again Wednesday nights. The churches take turns having Sunday morning services. I welcome any suggestions. My new friend Fred Thompson, M.E. pastor at Cairo, will be a big help."

Dan was welcomed warmly by his three Massac County churches. They were small and scattered. One church overlooked the Ohio River, another congregation had been formed just after the Civil War ended, and the third was a family church with deep community roots. Farmers, Civil War veterans and river boat workers populated his congregations. They liked Dan's hardest hitting sermons, "Keep telling us the truth about our being sinners!" A few warned, "No need using big, fancy words. We're just folks here!" Many, like his grandparents, came from Kentucky and Tennessee. They resented it when the state capitol was moved north to Springfield. Kentucky was closer to their hearts than Chicago.

But Chicago was on Dan's mind. Every day, he checked his mail, hoping for a letter from Chicago's Union Publishing Company. It was downtown on Washington Street, in the heart of the windy city. On Monday afternoon, October 9, Daniel stopped by the post office. The clerk asked, "Rev. Turney have you heard about Chicago?"

"Did my letter come?" Dan asked.

"No. Sorry. Chicago is burning."

"Burning. A fire in the city?"

"The whole place is on fire!"

It was not just a fire, but the biggest fire to ever char the Midwest. A wall of wind-driven flames destroyed thousands of buildings and killed hundreds of people. Downtown Chicago was reduced to a smoldering ash heap with a handful of surviving buildings that looked like blackened scarecrows in a field of death and destruction.

Dan thought about the people he'd met in Chicago the year before. Then it hit him. "My book. Union Publishing was in the heart of the city. It's gone. So are the plates and prints for my Sabbath Book. Lost. Burned!" Dan sat alone and wept like a baby. His book dream had gone up in smoke.

Dan struggled to preach the next Sunday, but managed to get through the day. After the evening service, he confided to a couple of farmers. One said, "Preacher, I know how you feel. I once had this prize sow hog and when it came time for her to farrow, all but two of her piglets were born dead. The next day, she accidently killed both of them by laying on them."

The other farmer chimed in with his own sad story, "We worked for a year clearing trees off a river bottom, so we could farm it. Blackest soil I'd ever seen. Planted corn and it grew high as an elephant's eye. Just before we went out to shuck it, the river flooded and we lost it all." Dan hoped the stories would end. But the second farmer had more to say. "I planted corn again the next year and raised the best crop I've ever had.

The first said, "I'm still raising hogs! Preacher, doesn't the Lord want us to keep trying and not give up?"

Dan accepted their advice and asked them to pray for him. They prayed long, loud and hard. When Dan got back to Metropolis, he sat in the rickety old rocking chair a neighbor had given him. He rocked back and forth and felt the disappointment, anger and despair begin to seep out of his soul. Before the week was over, he'd picked up his pen and begun to write. 'I'll write until I feel right again,' he told himself.

Area newspaper editors began getting letters from D.B. Turney. His letters kicked off a hornet's nest of responses. *The Cairo Bulletin* got so many letters about Turney that the editor accused answering ministers of being "envious" of him. The editor affirmed, "Mr. Turney knows he can write, and does write and writes well." Before winter's snow melted, Daniel B. Turney was becoming a legend of sorts in the southern tip of Illinois. Writing helped him to heal.

1872

Staunch bible believers in his churches lauded his preaching, until he meddled too much in prohibition or obsessed on baptism by sprinkling. Once, in a private conversation, Dan voiced an opinion, "We should have given full citizenship to women as well as slaves!" The word got out and didn't set well with the traditional 'Women should know their place' crowd. Most tolerated Dan's suffrage ideas because he was a young bachelor, who didn't know much about women. "He'll find out for himself, someday," said one old stalwart. A few tried to match Dan up with local girls, but that didn't work. He was outspoken, but also shy.

Dan wasn't shy about going to Cairo whenever he could, taking a steamboat or hitching a ride. He treasured time with Fred and Mollie Thompson and their first grader, Willie. He'd never been in a home with so much love and affection. The twenty-four-year-old bachelor preacher enjoyed Mollie's cooking. But her good cooking wasn't enough to keep her husband healthy. In late February, a weary Fred Thompson admitted, "I need to do something to restore my health and strength."

Dan advised, "I enjoy steaming down the Ohio. Maybe you need to take a boat trip, breathe in some fresh air."

A week later, Fred told him, "Captain Hambleton has offered me a bargain ticket to New Orleans on the good ship *Mary E. Forsyth*."

"When are you going?"

"Right after Easter, if I can find someone to cover Sunday night services."

Dan smiled, "I'd be happy to do that for you. I can make it over here for your 8pm service." Daniel preached Sunday nights in April. In July, Fred invited him to do some street preaching on the outskirts of town. The M.E. Conference wanted to develop an outreach mission on Cairo's north side. Dan relished the opportunity. Big crowds showed up, except for the night they got rained out. Fred told him, "Founder John Wesley would be proud of your open-air preaching! That's as Methodist as it gets."

Not everyone was happy with Dan. Some parishioners were enraged when he endorsed Republican presidential candidate Horace Greeley. Others disapproved of his plan to be a candidate for Superintendent of Public Instruction. One Sunday, late in the summer, M. E. Presiding Elder D.B. Pierce showed up unannounced to hear Dan preach. A handful of his critics pounced on the opportunity. An agitator invited Pierce to Sunday dinner and they feasted on roast preacher. Pierce was given newspaper articles written by D.B. Turney and a bigger batch of letters criticizing him as "the clerical idiot!" Dan learned about the betrayal and was so upset that he took the train from Metropolis back to Benton to talk with Grandpa Parish. Unfortunately, Grandma Parish was nearly on her deathbed. Dan knelt by her bedside to hear her whisper, "I love you Danny." Margaret Parish died the next morning. Braxton wept and Dan comforted him.

"She's at peace, at last, Danny. I'm so glad you were here with us." Dan felt his own tears burst forth. His grandfather comforted him, assuming they were grief tears. But the young preacher was also crying for his own future. He knew his grandmother was going to Heaven, but he didn't know where he was going.

After the funeral, he caught the last train south and got back to Metropolis in time to preach. Dan, weary with grief, churning with anger and numbed with fear stepped up to preach. He whispered the old farmer's wise words, "Keep trying and never give up."

Dan was still encouraged by this phrase when he went to Cairo, Illinois to preach at their Sunday night service. Many anticipated the sermon from Cairo's best-known letter writer. He tried not to disappoint them and felt he was among friends. A week later, he traveled to Mt. Vernon for the Annual Conference of the M.E. Church. This was Presiding Elder B.R. Pierce's home base. Daniel felt he was walking into the lion's den. When Dan met him in the hallway, Pierce looked the other way. When approval time rolled around, the rejection became official, "Daniel B. Turney's character is approved, but he is discontinued." It was a death sentence. His ministry in the Methodist Episcopal church was over, finished, dead. Ministers who knew Dan expressed regrets. Among them was Daniel Oglesby, a retired preacher who knew Braxton Parish. "Sorry to hear of your grandmother Margaret's death and sorry about today. What are your plans?"

"Guess I'll go home and pack." A firm hand on his shoulder spun him around.

Fred Thompson said, "Dan, you helped me in my hour of need. Now let us help you. Stay here in Cairo. Mollie and I will be glad to have you live with us. You are kin!"

Sheer relief flooded Dan, "Fred, that's more than I could ask for!"

"But not too much for us to offer!" Thompson exclaimed. "Mollie and I will get the spare room ready. Go back to Metropolis and pack your two shirts and your two-thousand books and come home to Cairo." Dan did so gladly.

CHAPTER TEN

Cairo
1872

Two days later, Mollie welcomed Dan, "Come on in. Fred is out making calls. Let me show you your room." He followed her through the parlor into a side room. "It's not very big," she apologized. Dan walked across the room to the bed in the corner. He touched the colorful quilt, glowing with patches of light from the early afternoon sun. Smiling, he pointed to the old desk and shelving for books. "Mollie, it's perfect. My old rocking chair will fit in the corner and there's room for most of my books!"

She replied, "I'm glad you like it. There isn't really a proper dresser, but Fred said you don't fret much about clothes."

"No, I don't. All I need are the ones on my back and a few extra unmentionables," he added, almost blushing.

By the time Fred got home for supper, Dan had moved in and stretched out on the bed. It was comfy and he closed his eyes. He jumped when Fred knocked on the doorframe. "Dan, you've moved right in!"

"Feel right at home, already!"

"Good. I'll see you at supper. Right now, I need to go rough house with Willie and keep him out of the kitchen."

"That how you help fix supper?" Dan asked.

"That's a father's job. If Willie is out of the way, Mollie can do her cooking magic." Fred walked back to the kitchen, "Willie, Willie boy, where are you?"

Dan sat on the bed trying to remember a single time when his father played with him before supper. L. Jay Turney had been more into politics than children. A gust of wind dinged the window with fall's first leaves. Dan stood up, walked to the window, leaned on the frame, lost in random thoughts. He looked beyond the drouth-stricken grass and thought about what the newspaper editor had written about him the week before. "Rev. Mr. Turney has ability. He has that critical sagacity which enables some men to find beauties and defects other men cannot see with a microscope. We have no doubt he could find a needle in a hay-mow full of hay- at night, before moonrise." Dan watched tumbling leaves and thought about lost needles.

"Mr. Turney, it's time for supper," a tiny voice called out. "I set out a plate and silverware for you."

"Thank you, Willie. I'll be right there."

After supper, Dan told Mollie, "That was a scrumptious feast!" He helped clear the dishes and asked Fred, "Do you have time for me to show you something in the morning?"

"You can count on it!" Fred said

After breakfast and getting Willie off to school, Fred said, "Dan, what did you want to show me?"

Dan said, "I'll get it." He walked back into the parlor carrying a package with a printer's logo, *B.O. Jones, Book and Job Printer.*

"What's in the bag?"

Dan hesitated, "I wish it was my Sabbath book, but it's just a pamphlet of my imagination. I want to give you a copy."

Fred glanced at the title, *The Mythifying Theory. Abraham Lincoln a Myth* by D.B. Turney. "That's a title and a half. I look forward to reading it. I'm not sure how, even you, can turn Abraham Lincoln into a myth?"

"Read it and you'll see," Dan said.

Two days later, Fred read Turney's pamphlet. "Some men have persisted in mythifying the Savior...I can come a thousand times as near the proof that Mr. Lincoln never existed, as all skeptics combined can, that Christ never was." Fred shook his head before turning the page and asked, 'Dan, how are you going to prove that?' He sighed when he read, "...Let us not be such bigots as to cling to Lincoln's actual existence, when we find conclusive evidence of the mythical nature of the supposed personage who is said to have liberated the slaves in the United States of America." Fred struggled to follow Turney's complex explanation of the hidden meanings in each letter of Abraham Lincoln's name that proved he was an "imaginary creature. He was a myth." It got more obtuse. "If he were not a mere myth, but a real person, how could his whole history be thus recorded in his name? The more this thought is examined, like a gristly-beefsteak, the tougher it appears...." Fred's headache got worse. "Count the letters in the name and multiply by the number of syllables. There are five syllables and fourteen letters...5 x 14 equals seventy." Fred tried to follow the convoluted argument through a wilderness of words. He was relieved to get to the last paragraph. "...There is a great deal better proof of the mythical nature of Mr. Lincoln, than all the infidels combined can bring forth as evidence against the existence of Jesus Christ, our Savior, as a real man."

Thompson rubbed his temples, 'Oh Dan, I already knew Jesus Christ was a real man, but I just can't think of Lincoln as a myth.'

The next day he worked up the courage to give Dan his honest opinion. Dan charged into the room. "Fred, I've been asked to speak at the Athenaeum next week!"

"Speak about what?"

"The political issues of the day! Grant and Greeley. Someone needs to speak up!"

"Dan, I'll be there."

On October 30, Fred walked into the Athenaeum, Cairo's massive auditorium. It was the biggest and most ornate facility in southern Illinois. Fred sat next to John Oberly, Cairo's newspaper publisher.

"Rev. Thompson, glad you're here. Turney may have been discontinued by the Methodists, but not by Cairo. It's going to be a memorable night!"

"Hope you are right, sir!" Fred shouted over the swelling crowd.

The crowd quieted as D.B. Turney stepped through the curtains and stood at the podium. He opened with a question, "Shall power and corruption choke down political honesty?" He named names and condemned "all the desperate scoundrels who would sell their country for gold, and Mexicanize our nation into discord and despotism…until civil liberty is destroyed and the vital energies of the republic are clamped forever…Four years ago, on account of his devotion to the nation and his military powers, I advocated Grant for the presidency; but today, owing to his employment of a dissolute and a ramified power of corruption in the damage of the union and his marked inefficiency and neglectfulness of duty, I advocate his defeat…." A thunderous applause swept the room, Both Thompson and Oberly were on their feet.

Turney continued, criticizing President Grant for using his power "to defeat the popular will and break down popular government. Ah! Little did I think this of General Grant four years ago! But do not the signs of the times show that he has resolved to sap the foundation of the republic and establish an imperialism on the ruins of our government?" Fred listened intently as Dan continued throwing verbal blows at the president. "Grant is a millionaire president with his brownstone houses, seaside cottages, hundred-thousand-dollar 'testimonials', copper interests, silver table-sets, railroad stocks, imported Havana's, hundred-and-fifty-dollar boots and Seneca sandstone quarry gleanings." Publisher Oberly frantically scribbled notes. Turney was talking faster than he could write.

Dan pumped his fist in the air, "No such whisky-steeped bundle of brass-mounted nepotism, avarice, ignorance, shall have my support for another four years' carousal at public expense!" The Cairo crowd was on its feet as Turney concluded, "I am not a sensationalist—never was called a sensational preacher, and do not want to be termed a sensational politician; but I sincerely believe that Grant is now working for an imperialism, and expects to reach it through gunpowder, desolation, bloodshed and destruction… his plans smack of treason!"

Oberly wrapped Thompson in a bear hug, "That was the best political oration I've ever heard!" He released Fred and rushed to the front. "I've got to get a copy of that speech!" Fred watched him thread his way toward the front and wondered, 'What's ahead for D.B. Turney? If Greeley gets elected, Dan might end up in D.C.'

But Grant beat Greeley and Turney stayed in Cairo. His Athenaeum speech recruited some fans and he received many invitations to speak and preach. The Cairo Bulletin often promoted his outings, "Turney will give another lecture." Sometimes he stirred the crowds with his words; sometimes he bored them. After a successful speaking engagement, Dan unloaded on Fred. "I still feel called to preach, but I do enjoy lecturing. Am I being called into politics?"

"No man can judge another man's calling, Dan. That's personal and private."

Dan retorted, "Then why has the M.E. church judged me and discontinued me?"

"The Cairo M.E. church still welcomes you. You and I have talked late into the night about reason, miracles and science. My flock would be interested in your ideas."

Dan's eyes brightened, "Have I ever turned down a chance to speak?"

"Not that I recall," Fred teased. "How about our Sunday evening service on March 2? Why don't you talk about the reasonableness of miracles?"

Dan hurried to his room and began sorting through his notes and books. Fred was steering him back to his preaching path. It worked.

1873

Dan's skillful weaving together the threads of God's miracles and human reason resonated with people. Cairo's newspaper commented: "Turney's lectures, which closed last night, have been pronounced by good judges as the most scientific and thorough of any ever delivered in Cairo. If published in book form, they would meet with ready sale. No mere synopsis can begin to do his lectures justice!"

Not everyone agreed with Turney's conclusion that "nature testifies to the bible theory of man's creation." Cairo's professor William Dennis disagreed vehemently through lectures and letters. It was a public debate for weeks. They disagreed, attacked and counter-attacked. Dan lumped Professor Dennis with Charles Darwin, accusing both, "We ask these men for proof, and they dish up conjecture; we call for facts and they furnish suppositions. We demand testimony! What a shameful attack on science to attempt to impose a law of evolution upon nature, in the face of her reiterated protests against the same. Is it possible to conceive of a more flagrant disregard of laws regarding scientific methods of research?" Turney described a British expedition that explored the ocean depths to find proof for the theory of evolution. "Did they find proof? No. Just the opposite. What will Mr. Dennis, the Darwinite of Cairo, say now? Theologians have not proven disloyal to science by rejecting the evolutionment; but scientists have claimed a tad-pole origin for themselves, finally to be shown what nonsense they have taught."

The Thompson's parsonage was now his home, but Dan minded his manners and always knocked before entering. Fred greeted him, waving the day's newspaper. "Dan, wait until you see this. Our friend John Oberly just declared you the winner of the evolution debate!"

He grabbed the paper and read for himself, "The Rev. Mr. Turney rushes again at Denton, and overturns the gentleman's theory of evolution."

"Look at his closing line."

Dan read it aloud, "Denton is gone, and D.B. remains master of the field."

"To keep you from getting too big-headed, Oberly gave you some free advice."

Daniel found it, "Friend Turney, always be brief. Remember that tedious old Polonius said: 'Brevity is the soul of wit.'"

"Even some of my best friends have told me that!"

"So, we have," Fred said. "Sit down, I want to talk to you about something else."

"I'll try to listen and be brief in what I say."

"You need some coffee? Let me get us some. While I fix it, read this letter."

Daniel unfolded the letter. "Rev. Fred Thompson, Rev. Daniel Turney and W.J. Grant--Congratulations, you have been approved as official delegates to the first delegated Sunday-School Convention in the state of Illinois. It will convene at Second Presbyterian Church in Springfield on Tuesday, May 27." He read through the detailed schedule until he smelled the coffee. Fred carried in two steaming cups. "This will be a historic convention and we get to be two of the first official delegates." Both had attended last year's overcrowded convention, which had to turn away hundreds. "How about I reserve train tickets to Springfield?"

Three weeks later they boarded an Illinois Central passenger car to Springfield. Fred napped his way north and Dan read a book. They made it to 2nd Presbyterian church just in time for the opening ceremonies. Thompson, a long-time supporter of cooperative Sunday School efforts, greeted old friends. Dan chatted with Alexander County's third delegate W.J. Grant. The convention began with a lively song-fest, a brief welcome from Springfield's mayor and a prayer offered by the church's pastor. After a financial report, they elected officers. Fred. L. Thompson of Cairo was elected to the executive committee. Dan pumped his hand with congratulations, but Fred shrugged it off.

During the lunch break, Fred excused himself, "Sorry, the executive committee has to meet during lunch. See you both this afternoon. Dan walked beside Grant, who teased, "Sorry my name is Grant and not Greeley. At least I'm not the corrupt Grant." Dan laughed. At lunch, they ran into an old friend of Grants. "Dan, I want you to meet a preacher friend from the old days, "Rev. W.H. Jordon. William, or as we called him 'Willie'." Dan shook his hand, "I'm Daniel B. Turney, Methodist preacher from Cairo,"

Jordon, beamed. "I'm a Methodist, too. Good to meet another of John Wesley's preachers. Are you Methodist Episcopal?"

"Yes, sort of...." Dan stuttered. Then he told Jordon the short version of his attempts to become an M.E. preacher.

Sympathetically, Jordon said, "Actually I'm in the Methodist Protestant branch of the Wesleyan tree. You've heard of us haven't you?"

Dan said, "I've met a few Methodist Protestants. All I know about M.P.s is that they don't much care for bishops."

"Why don't we talk some more during lunch. Will you join me?" Grant excused himself as Daniel sat across from Jordon. "No reason we can't eat Presbyterian chicken while we chew the fat about M.E.s and M.P.s."

Dan passed a biscuit and said, "Tell me more about the Methodist Protestants."

Still chewing his chicken, Jordon answered, "First of all, we are close kin to M.E.s. We're actually a twig off the M.E. branch. We're both rooted in the Wesleys, but we're growing in somewhat different directions."

"What do you mean?" Dan asked as he put a potato on his plate.

"Like, I was saying. We are very Methodist. But we're a little more Presbyterianish than you M.E.s. We don't have bishops. We don't have Presiding Elders overseeing districts. No superintendent tells a church they have to take a certain preacher and no preacher has to go to a church if he doesn't want to."

"Who decides which preachers go where? Dan asked

"The local church has more say in the M.P. way. It is more like a Presbyterian or Baptist call system. I'm biased, but I think we give lay people more authority. For instance, half the delegates at our annual conferences are laity. Back to your question about who decides who goes where. Each annual conference has a stationing committee that helps sort things out between churches and preachers. But the local church has the final say. M.P.s limit the power of clergy. I once heard someone say "We see the ministry as ministrative and not magistrative.""

"I like that," Dan said as he scribbled the phrase on a napkin. "I like a lot of what you say about Methodist Protestants. Could I be so bold as to ask you how someone becomes an M.P. preacher?"

"Certainly, but first, let me ask you a couple of questions." Jordon inquired about Dan's faith journey, his calling to preach and his commitment to Wesleyan ways. They talked about favorite books and swapped family stories. By the time Jordon had explained the basic steps into the ordained M.P. ministry, the dining room was empty. Jordon stood and pointed toward the door, "I imagine that the convention has started without us. But that's all right, that was the best talk I've had in weeks. Pray hard about what I said. You've got my address, if you want to take the big step, drop me a line."

"You'll be hearing from me!" Dan answered.

As they joined the stragglers hurrying into the afternoon session, Jordon added, "By the way, I'm currently on the stationing committee for the conference. I'll put in a good word for you!" Jordon stepped into the sanctuary. Dan pivoted and retraced his steps. 'I can't sit through reports and speeches. I need to think and pray.' He walked west down Monroe Street and stepped around puddles as he crossed the railroad tracks. The State Capital building looming on his left reminded him of his grandpa Parish's years in the Illinois legislature. Parish eventually left politics for preaching. Lost in reflection and prayer, Daniel B. Turney walked until he reached the edge of town. Just beyond Koke Mill Road, he walked over to a tree stump, knelt in the grass and poured out his heart in prayer. Only robins, searching for worms in the wet grass, witnessed Dan's private prayer meeting. When he finally stood, his knees were wet and cold, but his heart was warm and clear. He needed to talk with Fred and his grandfather before he wrote Jordon.

Dan confided with Fred on their southbound train trip. "That's wonderful!" Fred exclaimed. "My prayers are answered. You will be able to preach and stay a Methodist!"

"Rev. Jordon said M.P.s are just a small fast-growing branch of the big Methodist limb." They chatted all the way to the De Quoin station. "I'm getting off here. I need to talk with Grandpa Parish! I'll hike over to Benton and catch the late train back to Cairo tomorrow."

"See you then. God bless!" Fred said. He watched Dan grab his bag, heft it over his shoulder and rush down the aisle to the door.

In Benton, Dan retold his Springfield story. His grandparents were pleased. "We're glad you are staying in the Methodist fold and will be able to preach. When Dan got back to Cairo, he wrote William Jordon: "I want to become a Methodist Protestant preacher. Our conversation in Springfield and my thoughts and prayers since confirm this to God's calling. What papers or documents do I need to send you? I eagerly await your reply. Respectfully -Daniel Braxton Turney."

Sept. 1873

Three months later, D. B. headed to Brighton, just north of St. Louis, Illinois. Brighton's St. Paul church was hosting the 1873 Southern Illinois Methodist Protestant Annual Conference. Dan walked into the building, scanning the crowd to find William Jordon. A familiar voice rose above the buzz, "Dan. Dan Turney, over here!" Jordon was surrounded by a cluster of young men. "Come meet your new friends in the M.P. family. This is Amsbury Reynolds, fresh from Adrian, Michigan. Dan is joining us from the Methodist Episcopalians. He got his schooling in Wallamet, out in Oregon."

Reynolds gave Dan's hand a vigorous shaking, "You've come a long way. You must have a batch of stories to tell!"

"Yes, I do!" Dan replied. "Isn't Adrian M.P.s premier school?"

"That's what the alumni association claims." Reynolds said.

"We're about to get started," Jordon interrupted, "let me introduce you to the others who will be ordained into the Methodist Protestant ministry. Half a dozen men, shook his hand. "Gentlemen," Jordon said, "we've got two pews reserved for you up front." Dan sat with Reynolds, who asked, "How did you get from Oregon to Illinois?"

"Actually, I grew up in Illinois. When I was thirteen, we went west to the Washington Territory and ended up in Oregon. I came back here in '69 and started preaching in Little Egypt."

"Where's little Egypt?"

"Most of southern Illinois, like Egypt, once had bountiful harvests and shared grain with their drouth-stricken northern neighbors."

Reynolds said, "Like the Genesis story of Joseph in Egypt feeding his brothers?"

"That's it!" Dan said. "It's a good text to preach from here."

"Little Egypt. I'll remember that. Joseph's story is good anyplace!"

"Anytime"! Daniel added.

The song leader leapt to his feet and began belting out a hymn "O for a thousand tongues to sing!" Dan and Amsbury stood with the congregation and echoed the words back to the leader. Amsbury whispered, "I love Wesley's hymn, but glad we didn't sing all 18 verses of the original version." For two days, they sang, listened to sermons, endured reports and waited. When the ordination service came, Turney and Reynolds were ready. Dan walked up onto the platform and knelt. Methodist Protestant pastors circled him and placed hands on his head and shoulders, praying aloud for him to be empowered by the Holy Spirit. After the ordination, William Jordon hugged him, "The Lord bless you, brother Daniel!"

Before Conference ended, the stationing committee met with Dan and agreed on his appointment to Paris, Illinois on the eastern edge of the state, bordering Indiana. Dan was pleased that his new friend Reynolds would be serving in nearby Sumner, Illinois. "Amsbury, we'll be neighbors! You'll only be 30 miles south of Paris."

CHAPTER ELEVEN

Paris and Grandview, Illinois 1873

A week later, Dan was settling into Paris, a growing, bustling county-seat town, surrounded by fertile farm land. The St. Louis-Indianapolis rail line angled its way through town. The Methodist Protestant building was only a few years old and sat proudly on the east side of town. Pastors of the German Methodist and the Methodist Episcopal churches welcomed him. The community was friendly, but times were hard. Shortly before Dan moved in, a national financial crisis was triggered on Black Thursday. It shut down the stock market for ten days and kicked off what was called *The Panic of '73'* and *The Great Depression.* In his sermons, Dan offered hope to a discouraged people, "We do not live by bread alone, but by the enduring word of God. As we trust in the Lord, the Lord will provide."

One day he was approached by a ragged, dirty young vagabond who had been train-hopping across Indiana. He begged, "Sir, could you give me a dime?"

Dan looked deep into his eyes and asked, "My friend, what is your name?"

"Fred W. Jones," he said.

"Well, Mr. Jones," Dan remarked, "you seem to be having a rough time of it and perhaps the Lord Jesus has sent you to me to be helped and started on the right road." Dan took him to a little diner and bought him dinner, then took him to a store and bought him a new suit of clothes, shirts and a hand satchel. Handing him a ten-dollar bill and a bible, Dan said, "Mr. Jones, read this book, put your trust in the Redeemer it discloses, keep up your courage and when you get able— as you will—pass on to some other fellow being the same help which I have given you. Remember that Jesus said, 'Let not thy left hand know what thy right hand doeth,' and that God rewards his servants in his own way."

Dan saw a new jaunt in Jones' step as he walked back to the train track. 'I pray he will become a winner in the fight of life and not give up.' On Sunday morning, the congregation knew a new fire had been lit in Dan. Their new preacher was a man of surprises. Turney often painted glimpses of brilliance on a canvas of impracticality. A church leader said, "He is the smartest preacher, I've ever heard, but I don't think he has a lick of common sense." Another complained, "I agree with the newspaper guy who said Turney 'is a genius, with a screw loose somewhere.'" His support began unravelling.

1874

Turney still had fans back in Cairo. He was invited to return and give one of his famous lectures. The Cairo newspaper opined that some of the community would be dismayed because they feared Dan's rhetoric. "He is a hammer of the gospel, and when he descends, he smashes infidelity—smashes it into very small pieces. Mr. Turney has frequently assured us this is a fact...."

Dan traversed southern Illinois, promoting temperance and even threw his hat in the ring for the 19th district congressional seat. His Paris church, wearied of his hammering away at certain pet issues, asked for a different preacher. In September, Dan moved ten miles west of Paris to serve Grandview. The smaller congregation gave him more time for community involvement, writing and speaking. He intensified his interest in the prohibition movement and got involved in the county committee, then the state committee. People were impressed when they discovered that he had attended the Party's founding meeting in Chicago in '69. Dan's reputation was growing. He was invited to speak at a tri-county event in Effingham and gladly accepted.

Daniel Braxton Turney climbed the stairs to the platform and took a deep breath. A noisy crowd packed the hall for the prohibition rally. He was surprised at how many women were in the room. It was a big crowd, Saturday night loud; waiting to be challenged, daring the speaker to jog their minds with a breeze of words strong enough to blow away the cobwebs of daily life.

Dan opened with a question. Before anyone could respond, he answered it himself. Then he fired off another question followed by his answer. After a few rounds of this, the crowd got into it and began shouting back, trying to beat him to the punch. Dan was pleased with himself as he launched into the body of his speech, which promoted both prohibition and suffrage. He wrapped it up with a call to action. It was part political speech and part sermon. He gave no altar call, but a bunch of people surged forward for more. It was an excited circle, spinning ideas, searching for answers. Most were younger than Daniel. Several women made observations and asked questions. He enjoyed the limelight, until he thought of his mother's recent question, "How can an eligible bachelor have so many women flocking around him and still have no sweetheart?" She was right. Here he was talking to scores of women about suffrage, but he was suffering from having no woman. One woman in the group caught his attention. In the lantern light, he could see that she was pretty, with her brown hair bound tight in a fashionable bun. Her clothes were modest and she wore no jewelry. Her eyes met his.

"Dr. Turney?" she stepped forward cautiously.

"No doctorate, yet," he answered.

"Could you settle a dispute I'm having with my friends? They think you cannot be the same D.B. Turney who has become famous for so many letters in the Effingham newspaper. I say you are one and the same!"

Dan replied, "That's easy to settle. I am that man. The 'D' is for Daniel and the 'B' is for Braxton. I was named for my grandfathers. May I ask your name, Miss?"

"Emma V. Oglesby. My father's name is also Daniel."

Dan inquired, "Would that be Rev. Daniel Oglesby, Methodist Episcopal preacher down in Richview?'"

"One and the same," she replied. "But I don't live in Richview anymore. I live in Redmon, just a few miles north of your church. She blushed, but didn't lose eye contact.

Emma's group was drifting away, but she lingered. Dan was glad the shadows hid his blushing face. Then, in an unusual act of social boldness, he asked, "Miss Oglesby, I was wondering if I might... ah.... see you?"

With a twinkle in her blue eyes, she replied, "Of course. You probably need a woman's perspective on women's suffrage."

Dan stuttered, "You have a point, Miss Oglesby."

She touched his arm and said, "Why don't you call me Emma. Do I call you sir, your highness of ideas, Mr. Wordsmith or just Dan?" She almost giggled. He didn't know what to say. She filled the awkward silence, "How about I call you Dan?" She squeezed his arm, "Are you going to come courting on Sunday?" He blurted, "Yes. How about after church?"

"That will be fine. I don't have far to come and I have a gentle horse and one of my daddy's buggies. He's read some of your writings and thinks you are quite a thinker, even if you jumped ship to become a Methodist PROTESTANT."

"I can explain that," Dan muttered.

"I am sure you can," she said. "But not tonight. My friends are waiting for me."

Dan saw them waving.

Emma started toward them, but turned back to him, "Sorry, I must go. See you Sunday Dan. Don't make your sermon too long or we won't have time to enjoy my basket lunch." He nodded, a deer in her headlight.

The Sunday basket lunch became a tradition with Dan and Emma. People were no longer surprised to see them together. Sometimes they talked, but as often they sat together under their favorite oak tree and read books. Emma had been taught by her father and mother to love books. She did. But she had never met anyone who was as book crazy as her Daniel B. She accused him of first telling her, "Emma, I think I love you!" without looking up from the book he was reading.

She told him, "I hope you love me as much as you love that bag of books you tote around everywhere you go." He gave her a squeeze, but couldn't help glancing at his book bag.

1875

A few months later, Dan borrowed a buggy and rode to Richview, Illinois to ask Rev. Daniel Oglesby for Emma's hand in marriage. Oglesby towered over Dan, but greeted him warmly. "Welcome. My Emma brags about your speeches and sermons." He winked, "Says you're almost as good a preacher as her daddy!" Dan accepted the offer to sit on the porch swing.

Oglesby sat beside him and said, "You wrote me at Christmas saying you wanted to ask me something,"

"Yes, sir I do." Turney replied nervously.

"What is it, boy, you change your mind about bishops and are ready to come back to the Methodist Episcopal fold?"

"No sir, I want to ask for Emma's hand in marriage."

The old preacher smiled and grasped Dan's hands, "That can be arranged. Welcome to the family!"

On April 14, 1875, Daniel Braxton Turney returned to Richview, Illinois and stood beside his bride Emma Virginia Oglesby. A handful of friends and family surrounded them. A life-long friend of the Oglesby's, Dr. James Finley, president of McKendree College, led them through the brief marriage ceremony. He concluded, "I pronounce you husband and wife."

Two weeks later, they were home in Grandview. Dan was bent over his desk, writing furiously. Emma sat on the bed across the room. "What are you writing about, Mr. Turney?

He smiled, "It's a tome about you, Mrs. Turney."

"Better be saying sweet things."

"Someday, you'll see for yourself," he teased.

"Why don't you put out that lamp, come over here and whisper me some of those sweet things." Dan was blushing as he pulled back the covers and crawled into bed with her. She tried, but couldn't charm him to reveal his secret words.

Emma had to wait a week to discover what he'd written. Dan brought the mail into the kitchen and handed her an envelope he'd torn open. She pulled out a newspaper clipping from his hometown paper, *The Wayne County Press*. Her eyes fell on a letter to the editor entitled, "Dan Rejoiceth." She read it aloud, "I've beaten the tom-tom and sounded the hewgag of matrimony. The event has transpired and the ceremony was said on the 14th day of last month. Light and joy attend me, Pleasure and peace fold their arms around me. A baptism of blessing besprinkles my brow and comfort crowns my life." She glanced at him, blushed and continued reading, "The late Emma Virginia is now Mrs. D.B. Turney. So, you see, I have captured 'Virginia' without firing a gun or fighting a battle; and if that isn't good generalship, what is?"

She hugged him, then stepped back. "Sweet words, General Turney, until you bragged about capturing Virginia. Sir, this suffragette is not a territory to be conquered!" Dan's face dropped as he realized his clever words had drowned his sweet words. Capturing Virginia was such a clever phrase to think, but dumb to say.

Later, while Emma worked in the garden, Dan reread his clever regretted letter. He was tempted to wad it up and throw it away, but saw that the editor added his own words of congratulations, "Our unparalleled astonishment at the above is only equaled by the immensity and exuberance of our profound congratulations, herewith tendered…." Dan decided to save the clipping. Then he opened the rest of his mail. *The American Woman's Friend* wrote, "Our famous correspondent in Illinois, D.B. Turney, whose articles have created more sensations than a thousand balloon ascensions, has done a very foolish thing. He has taken unto himself a wife- without consulting us, and he didn't send us a slice of the wedding cake."

Turney talked back to the editor, "Sorry, but the crumbs would not have mailed well." He continued reading, "The history of the movement of extending suffrage to women will encircle the name of Turney with a radiance that will never cease. Those very able articles in favor of woman suffrage signed 'Xenia' are from his pen."

'Another of my secrets exposed,' Dan thought as he opened the next envelope and read a clipping from *Vine Grower's Journal*. "Wonders never cease. Turney is married- D. B. Turney! He says he has the most lovely woman in this great American nation. Maybe! If so, we allow our eyes to melt for her. She has the most unlovely man. He is the perfect Ishmaelite- at war with everybody. He fights against the leading benevolent orders of the day...debates incessantly-pitches into everybody who differs from him and has very enticing ways of making folks hate him. He is a temperance fanatic- an anti-tobacco enthusiast- a hot-headed woman's rights apostle- an anti-episcopal methodist- always travels with the brakes off and lives in constant commotion. His scholarship can't be denied, but his way of using that scholarship is most objectionable." Dan had heard it before and knew much of it was true.

He hoped the next letter would be better. It was. *The Massac Journal* article commented on his marriage. "We know Dan. He is the intellectual peer of any man in America, and is governed in all he does by the simple, persistent sense of duty. He has some egotism, but no more than his competency warrants." He felt like he'd been patted on the back and pinched at the same time.

There was one last envelope. A clipping from *The Berkshire Banner* said, "The modern Plutarch, D.B. Turney, has become a benedict at last. Cupid twanged his bow on the 14th of April, 1875, and Miss Emma V. Oglesby became Mrs. D.B. Turney in a jiffy...." Before he had finished, Emma walked through the mud room door, wiping her hands on her apron. She had cooled down, but couldn't resist, "Still reading, General Turney?"

He felt like a kid caught with his hand in the cookie jar. "It's just another newspaper clipping."

Emma took it and read aloud, "So cupid twanged his bow and I became Mrs. D.B. Turney in a jiffy. Wait there is more." She read silently, then laughed. "I love the last line, 'We hope she will be able to manage Turney. We never could.' Daniel B. Turney, I don't reckon I'll ever be able to manage you, but I hope I can keep loving you."

Emma couldn't even manage to keep him in Grandview for a month. Dan caught a westbound train to Princeton, Illinois to spend two weeks as one of Southern Illinois' two clergy delegates to the Methodist Protestant General Conference. Dan shrugged when Emma accused him of being as excited about the conference as he had been about their wedding day.

On May 19th, he rushed into the Princeton church jammed with 100 representatives from all over the U.S.A. Dan sat next to John Robison from New Jersey, who said, "This is a historic session. The M.P. church has never held General Conference this far west before."

"Our church is growing westward," Dan observed.

The first day had little to do with growth and more to do with organizing, reports and schedules. Dan dodged boredom by scribbling a resolution for tomorrow's session. The next morning, he stood and made his motion that "a committee of three ministers and three lay persons be appointed by the president of the General Conference on the question of the ordination of women in the M.P. Church and the authorization of that ordination in the Word of God and in the Book of Discipline." His motion was tabled until three in the afternoon.

As he returned to his seat, the conference secretary called him over. "Rev. Turney, would you honor us by leading our religious services at 2 pm?" Dan skipped lunch to prepare, scribbling notes on the back of his program. Suddenly it was 2pm. He put all his energies into leading the service. He realized he had preached too long when the chair said, "Thank you brother Turney. Unfortunately, time constraints won't allow us to consider your resolution. We must return to the order of the day and proceed with the nomination committee report." Procedures and minor motions gobbled up the rest of the day. Dan was adrift in a complex system and couldn't figure out how to get women preachers back on the agenda.

On Saturday morning he got another opportunity. President Burnes said, "I have received a resolution that D.B. Turney of Southern Illinois prepare a paper on water baptism. All in favor, raise your hands." It passed. Dan rubbed his hands together in expectation. But before he could write a word, a committee raised a question, "Is water baptism essential to admission into full connection with the church? According to our Discipline, the answer is 'Yes'!" That launched a lively debate. Most agreed with the committee. But Lowden of Indiana claimed, "The conditions of church membership are *Christian experience* and not *Water baptism!*"

Dan couldn't resist jumping in, "Are there more qualifications for admission into the Methodist Church than into Heaven? What the Book of Discipline says about water baptism and membership is at war with the spirit of progress and liberty of conscience so thoroughly inculcated in the Bible."

He was too busy crafting his words to sense the disagreement in the room. They expressed their disapproval by tabling the half dozen motions Dan tried to make before adjournment.

He boarded the train, deflated and depressed. Emma welcomed him home with a hug and a reprimand, "Daniel Braxton, your antics in Princeton made the news. Bad news, I fear."

"Not my finest hour," he admitted. "I felt like I was climbing up the face of a cliff while the crowd above threw rocks down at me." Emma comforted him. She could see the bruises.

Three months later, he needed her comfort even more. Dan's beloved grandfather Braxton Parish died on August 16. Dan fought back tears, "I hope I can be half the preacher he was!"

Emma said, "Dan, it's right to grieve, but we grieve in the hope of the resurrection!" He knew she was right, but cried anyway. She wiped a tear from his cheek and whispered, "God will wipe away all tears from our eyes." The promise of Revelation 7:17 comforted him.

CHAPTER TWELVE

Bond County, IL

Two weeks later, his grief was subdued and life moved on. Dan and Emma were in a train rumbling west toward Greenville, Illinois. Emma touched his hand, "Dan, your grandpa would be so proud of you. You'll be speaking to your third Prohibition Rally since we got married."

He squeezed her hand. "I'm glad you're going with me, Em!"

A large crowd welcomed them and he discovered there were many enthusiastic Methodist folks in Bond County. They opposed the breweries in nearby St. Louis, which profited from 'demon rum'. Daniel preached with fire. Afterwards, three zealous members of the Methodist Protestant church cornered him, "Would you come to Bond County and be our preacher? People can't believe unless they hear and they can't hear without a fired-up preacher who rightly handles the word of the Lord!"

Dan, warming to their passion, blurted out, "I am called to preach that life-giving word!"

Emma watched Dan being swept up by the moment. She tried to caution him, but it was too late. He did not yet understand what her arm squeeze meant. D.B. Turney had already bonded himself to preach in Bond County. He could not understand Emma's silence on their train ride back to Edgar County, so he read a book. She pondered her choice of marrying a man who was so bright, but so vulnerable to flattery. 'God help me,' she prayed.

The next day, she wrote her father about their possible move. She only hinted at her frustrations, but knew he had a way of reading between the lines. His answer shocked her. "Dan! Dan!" she burst into his study. "How could I have forgotten?" He was bewildered. She waved the letter. "Dad just wrote me about Bond County. I forgot that I'd lived there when I was a child. Dad preached in Dudleyville and helped build their church. It's a little town just south of Greenville. Now I know why Greenville seemed familiar!"

"It'll be like going home?" Dan said.

"Yes. That was why I got so excited! God keeps surprising me."

"Me, too!" Dan said. He pushed aside his books and gave her a big hug. It was a relief to have his Emma back again.

But they weren't finished with disappointments. When the stationing committee contacted Dan, he learned that the Methodist Protestant Church that invited him to preach was not located in the county seat of Greenville, but in the village of Woburn. "There is some good news." Dan told Emma, "They want me to establish a regular preaching place in Greenville and the M.P. building in Woburn is just four years old."

They said goodbye to Edgar County and boarded the St. Louis to Indianapolis rail line for another trip to Bond County. John Glenn and his wife Mary Jane met them at the train station in Greenville. They loaded boxes of books, bundles of clothing and a few pieces of furniture into Glenn's big buckboard. The four of them crowded together on the bench. Glenn snapped the reigns and began to tell Dan the church's history, "Rev. William Collins was our first preacher. My folks were Methodist Protestants back in North Carolina and wanted a M.P. church here. Mom, dad, the Klines, Enloes and Washburn's worked together from the beginning. You already met Thomas Kline and Thomas Enloe."

"At the Rally?"

"Yes, sir. Before we had a proper church building, we worshipped in each other's homes. I was just knee high to a grasshopper back then. We met for a while in a schoolhouse. We outgrew that, so we built our church in Woburn." He rolled up his left sleeve. "See that scar? Got it putting up a rafter in the entryway."

"John," Glenn's wife cautioned, "Rev. and Mrs. Turney don't need to hear our whole history before they even get to town." Emma smiled. She had experience trying to slow down a talkative husband.

Glenn continued, "Mary Jane, before we get there, we best explain the town name."

"Yes. It is confusing. Some folks still call it Newport."

Emma was confused.

"Newport is what settlers first named the town. Everyone got used to the name, then discovered there was already an Illinois town named Newport. Getting mail got to be a mess, so they changed the name to Woburn."

Glenn added, "But maps still have both names, *Newport/Woburn P.O.* Whatever name you call it, we're almost there. Mary Jane, want explain to them about their house?"

Mary Jane said, "Sorry, we did the best we could, but the house is kind of run down. We haven't had a preacher living in town for a spell."

"Had our hands full, building the church," John interjected.

"Anyway, I wish it was in better shape!" Mary Jane apologized again.

The house wasn't as bad as Emma feared. It was small and smelled like it hadn't been lived in for a while. But it was swept clean and there was a big pile of fresh-cut firewood near the back door. After unloading the Turney's belongings, Mary Jane invited them to supper. "It'll take me a spell to fix, but you two can rest up."

"I can help you," Emma said.

John offered, "Rev. Turney, why don't we stretch our legs. I'll show you the church. It's just a couple blocks away."

"Sounds good, John."

"My friends call me Johnny, preacher."

"And you can call me Dan!"

When the men walked away, Emma put her hand on Mary Jane's arm. "Can I talk to you about something private?"

"Of course, Mrs. Turney."

"Please call me Emma. What I wanted to tell you is that I am with child. Our first."

Mary Jane hugged her, "Bless you, sister. Moving is hard enough without being in the family way. We'll help you get through this." She was true to her word and helped Emma unpack and settle in. Dan was off on a two-week preaching expedition over in Lawrence Co., Illinois.

After a week, she got one of his effusive letters, "My dear Emma, Amsbury Reynolds seems to have the good will of his people. Hope I can learn from him. But for now, I'm on the war-path, fighting the good fight of faith. Reynolds invited me to lay siege to the citadels of such enemies as are entrenched down here. I am assisting him in bringing the large field-ordinance to bear on the super-clergian forts. I will return Friday. All my affection, Dan."

1876

Emma shook her head, 'Dan, Dan. You and your words!' She told Mary Jane, "My husband never uses a small word if he can find a bigger one." Mary Jane proved to be a loyal friend and was with Emma and Dan on the cold February morning when Mary Elizabeth Turney was born. Woburn's only doctor helped with the delivery. Emma slipped into an exhausted sleep listening to the new father announce, "February 21, 1876 is a historic day!! She was almost born on Washington's birthday." Mary Jane tried to calm Dan, "Why don't you write your baby girl a welcome letter? I'll hold Mary Elizabeth." She cuddled and cooed to the newborn and Dan wrote her a letter. Emma slept.

Spring came. Emma's world was confined to her new baby, the tiny house and a big garden, Dan's world expanded beyond Woburn and Greenville to north central Ohio, where he had been challenged to a debate on baptism.

After speaking to excited crowds in Mansfield, Ohio, little Woburn seemed dull to Dan. Emma cautioned, "Grass looks greener on the other side of the fence, but looks can be deceiving."

"True," Dan admitted, "but a good shepherd looks for greener grass and more sheep." As an obedient wife, Emma bit her tongue. She would miss Mary Jane.

CHAPTER THIRTEEN

Ohio
Nov. 1876

The Turneys rumbled and shook across Illinois, through Indiana and into Ohio. Eight-month-old Mary Elizabeth was rocked to sleep, then jolted awake. The screech of the train's brakes didn't agree with her tender ears. Her whimpers were drowned by the conductor's booming voice, "Jeffersonville". Next stop, "Columbus!" Emma nursed the fussy baby when she could, but the train's schedule did not match the youngest passenger's feeding pattern. Dan was a stranger to the ways of fussy babies. "Emma, God knew what He was doing when he made women and not men to care for babies."

The tired young mother replied, "So we're smart enough to care for your progeny, but not to vote!"

"You know I believe that women should have the right to vote!"

"Sorry, Dan," she apologized, "Right now I need to sleep more than I need to vote."

He gave her shoulder a squeeze, "We'll be there soon. Should I hold Mary Elizabeth and let you get some rest?"

Emma smiled, "She and I will both rest better if I hold her." Before nodding off, she confessed, "I hope and pray that Ohio treats us well." Emma and the baby slept, while the preacher pondered his decision to go east. This was his second train ride from Woburn, Illinois to Mansfield, Ohio. Two months ago, he had come to Ohio for a debate about baptism. His debate skills had been sharp in the sultry late-summer heat in Mansfield's Christian Church. Elder Clark Braden proved to be a formidable foe. But Dan expounded the validity of infant baptism and sprinkling with a profundity that confounded his host church and debate opponent. Most of the audience agreed with Braden that adults should be baptized by immersion and that baptizing children didn't really count. It was an ongoing debate between Methodists, who often baptized by sprinkling water on a baby's head, and Christian church folks who insisted on immersing adults all the way under the water. People from all over Richland County flocked to Mansfield to watch the debate and marvel at Turney's clever way with words.

William Albright challenged Dan, "Preacher, you've been saying what Richland County needs to hear! We Methodist Protestants have only small churches with weak voices and don't have a church here in Mansfield. We'd like you to start one. You could preach Sundays at Independence and Butler, while you plant a new congregation here. We can't pay much, but we do our best. We have a parsonage in Independence. What do you think?" Dan inhaled the fumes of evangelistic potential and felt God calling him to start a new church. It was in his blood. He was Braxton Parish's grandson.

A jolt on the tracks awoke Dan to reality. 'I hope I'm not just escaping my failures in Illinois.' He kept his doubts a secret; Emma had enough to deal with. Three stops later, the conductor announced, "Mansfield. Mansfield, Ohio." Dan and Emma stood; Mary Elizabeth cried. On the platform, they were greeted by one man with a horse and buggy. William Albright shook Dan's hand vigorously, touched Emma's arm and tickled the baby's tummy. While Albright explained some things to Dan, Emma rocked the baby and wondered how the rickety buggy could hold four people and four moving trunks. The husky farmer was surprised at how heavy the trunks were.

"My books." Dan explained.

"Reckon you have to read a lot to preach like you do, Rev. Turney!"

Emma thought, 'If only you knew how much he reads.' Dan held the baby while she climbed into the buggy. He put the baby in her lap and sat beside her. Albright said, "Sorry, we're so crowded." He snapped his whip and the horse strained under the weight of his new cargo. "The church had a pounding last Sunday and we stocked your kitchen and pantry with pumpkins, squash, beans, honey, fresh bread and a cured ham."

January 1877

Dan fashioned a study of sorts in a corner of the parsonage's front room. Books and papers covered furniture and spilled out on to the floor. Emma tapped him on the shoulder and whispered, "Come to the kitchen and watch Mary Elizabeth. She took her first step." Dan walked to the kitchen, leaned on the door frame and waited. He was rewarded by seeing his birthday girl take two steps before falling. She began to cry. He went to pick her up but Emma stopped him. "She's fine. Just one of life's little bumps!" Mary E. crawled back to Emma and pulled herself up by grabbing Emma's skirt.

A week later, they applauded when she made it half-way across the room. Emma told Dan, "I got good news today. My sister Nancy got married and is moving to Mt. Vernon, Illinois. I'm so happy for her!"

"Your Dad approved?"

"Yes! He even officiated at the wedding. I wish I could have been there.

Mary Elizabeth lunged into Emma's outstretched arms. Emma hugged her tightly, "Momma love's you."

The toddler touched her face, "Ma, Ma...." Tears streamed down Emma's cheeks. Dan felt tears well up in his eyes. Emma had just told him he was going to be a father again.

The spring flowers bloomed with promise. Emma dreamed of life for Mary and for the child growing within her. Dan dreamed of getting the new Mansfield church started. "Emma, today I convinced a county official to give us a permit for an outdoor public gathering. We poor M.P.s can't afford to rent a building."

Emma asked, "Didn't your street preaching work back in Cairo? Maybe it will work here in Ohio!"

"I hope so. We plant, but God gives the growth." He lovingly patted her stomach, "Speaking of growth."

She swatted his hand away and stood, "I've got to check on Mary Elizabeth. She's not been feeling like herself this week."

Minutes later, Emma called out, "Dan, come in here and feel her forehead." Dan agreed, "She's hot." In the afternoon they noticed a red bumpy rash on her back. Mary Elizabeth rubbed her head and cried. She had trouble swallowing and didn't want to eat. The second time the doctor examined her, he said, "I'm afraid she has scarlet fever."

"What can we do?" Emma pleaded.

"Keep her cool and comfortable. Lots of fluids. You'll just have to wait."

"Wait and pray." Dan said, trying not to use his preacher's voice.

They waited and prayed as the fever burned away the life of their sweet little girl. She died Monday morning, April 30th. Daniel grieved, but he'd never seen anything like the grief Emma felt. Her faith was shattered, "Why has God forsaken us? Why?" Dan couldn't think of anything to say. Emma didn't eat, couldn't sleep and refused to pray. Dan tried to pray, but words wouldn't come. On Sunday, he mumbled his way through his sermon. Emma got worse. Then she lost her unborn baby. Stillborn. Dead. The doctor told them it had been a boy.

Emma sobbed uncontrollably, but Dan had no tears. He was angry. "We must give our son a name!" She was stone silent. He continued, "He is now in the Lord's hands, but we still need to name him." She shook her head. He pressed, "Then I will name him. Metta. Metta Turney." She gave him a blank look. "Meta in Greek means 'beyond' or 'after'. Our son is beyond this life. He has entered the after-life."

The next morning, Dan announced, "I'm going to the *Shield and Banner* newspaper office."

"Whatever for?" she asked.

"To ask them to run an obituary for our son!"

Emma threw up her hands, "No you won't! Don't do that!"

"I must!" Dan answered. "There is nothing else we can do for him, but we can do that! Our son's life mattered!" She was still shaking her head when he bolted out the door.

Metta's tiny obituary was printed in the newspaper two days later. Emma wouldn't speak to Dan for a week and stewed in her grief for weeks. Dan refocused his energies on starting the new church in Mansfield. By late July, Emma had healed enough to read the newspaper without thinking about the forbidden obituary. Her heart skipped a beat when she read, "Daniel Braxton Turney will preach (providence permitting) from the steps of the Mansfield Courthouse on Monday, July 30."

She traveled with him to Mansfield. "I can always count on you Em," he told her before climbing the courthouse steps. A crowd gathered- church members, neighbors, the curious and hecklers. "My subject tonight is *Preach the Word!* 'Hear, O Heavens, and give ear, O earth; for the Lord hath spoken; I have nourished and brought up children and they have rebelled against me.' We have a right to set a high estimate upon human reason; but we must not overvalue the treasure. Reason must have correct premises to go upon...."

"What premises?" a heckler shouted.

Dan preached on, "True religion comes holding the Bible in her hands, and urging us to examine its evidence. We are called upon to exercise reason to establish the truth of the sacred volume. The Bible professes to come from God...."

"Can you prove that?" someone yelled.

"Our fathers and forefathers... have conscientiously revered this book!" Daniel waved his bible. "Philosophers have bowed their heads, to acknowledge that this is the most profound and sublime of all books, and worthy of general credence; that the good have been guided by it; the vicious reformed through it, and the dying cheered by it. I want to thank the gentleman in the back row for his question. We see that it is not customary for sensible and polished men to entertain serious doubts as to its divine authenticity."

He finished with an invitation. A handful of people stayed after the sermon, but most scattered quickly. A friend from church put his hand on Dan's shoulder, "You gave it your best, preacher..." Dan tensed. "This was a tough crowd. Afraid we didn't make much headway tonight." On the way home, Emma agreed.

"I'm not giving up!" Dan said. "I'm preaching there again next Monday!" The crowd shrank, but hecklers grew. The only visible fruits for his effort were the tomatoes thrown at them. The Methodist Protestants cleaned up the mess. When he asked the newspaper editor for another promotional announcement, he was told, "Rev. Turney, you're not a paying customer and my paper has important news to cover and tomatoes on the courthouse steps are not newsworthy." Without publicity, crowds dwindled; even the harassers disappeared. Dan gave up street preaching and retreated to his study.

"What are you writing?" Emma asked

"My rebuttal of psychomancy."

"What in the world is that?" she asked.

"Here's what I wrote, 'It is very certain that the spirits of the saved are in heaven, or paradise, in the enjoyment of the rest prepared for them that love the Lord. They are not rambling around our world and tipping tables...Those persons who believe in the possibility of seeing ghosts, are the people who see such things...advancing science...will in due time put to flight the vagrant ghosts that materialize under the order of mediumistic associations...The pro and con of Modern Spiritism will most undoubtedly all be found to rest in the knotty skeins of the fundamental sophisms, which I have been here to unravel.'"

"Dan, you always have some bee buzzing in your bonnet. That drew me to you, but sometimes it drives me crazy!"

He huffed, "Bees make the honey you like in your tea, my sweetheart!"

She went back to the kitchen and he put the finishing touches on his thirteen-page pamphlet. He wrote a letter to Rev. George Roork in Oregon explaining his latest brainstorm and finished an inquiry letter to a friend in West Virginia, "Do you have any M.P. churches that need a preacher?"

CHAPTER FOURTEEN

West Virginia
Fall 1877

A week later, a reply came from West Virginia. "Yes, we need preachers. I've put your name into the hat." They exchanged letters and the Turneys headed to a new pastorate in Grafton, West Virginia. Emma confessed, "I barely know West Virginia from Virginia and I've never heard of Grafton." It was mountainous coal country, dotted with mining towns and small churches. They had barely settled in at Grafton when one of Dan's provocative letters was published in the *Wheeling Daily Intelligencer*. It stirred up the simmering baptismal controversy in Grafton. Baptists and Church of Christ folks jumped all over Dan's parishioners.

A disgruntled church member complained, "Rev. Turney, you've got that fancy schoolin' and all, but we have to get along with our neighbors who baptize by dunking adults and refuse to baptize babies."

"Let me show you what the bible says!" Dan opened his Greek New Testament.

The church member pushed aside Dan's bible, "We believe in Jesus and the King James and not that Greek gobbledygook."

Dan was stumped. He had stirred up a hornet's nest in Grafton. Both Turneys were out of sorts. Emma was recovering from morning sickness and couldn't shake her homesickness for Illinois. "Dan, I just want to go home. I want to be with my kinfolk when this little one is born."

"Can't we make this our home?"

"I've tried, Dan. My sister Nancy wrote me again and offered for me to stay with them in Mt. Vernon." After seeing the look on his face, she added, "After the baby comes, we'll come back here."

Dan conceded, "If you think it's for the best, we can get you a train ticket back to Illinois."

She hugged him.

Sept 1878

On September 29, 1878 Emma gave birth to John Edward Zuriel Turney in Stratton, Illinois, near Mt. Vernon. Her sister was by her side. Both rejoiced that the baby was alive and healthy. Emma's father Daniel Oglesby and her stepmother visited and took turns holding baby John. Back in West Virginia, Dan settled into a lonely bachelor's routine.

1879

He was relieved to pick up Emma and Johnny at the train station in late July. Dan and Emma were glad to be together, but little Johnny wasn't sure what to make of this doting stranger. In a few weeks, Dan won over his son, but he was not winning over the Grafton church folks. Critics became so disgruntled that they brought formal charges against Rev. D.B. Turney. The West Virginia Annual Conference meeting August 27th would examine the evidence and decide his fate.

Emma waved to Dan as he hitched a ride west to the dreaded conference in St. Marys on the Ohio River. The six days dragged by slowly. Emma was glad she had a child and chores to distract her. On September 2, she nursed Johnny, put him to bed and waited nervously on the porch. Dan tried to assure her that everything would work out. "Emma, the worst thing that could happen is that we'll have to move," She had retorted, "Or we have to stay here where we're not wanted!"

Both bad choices nibbled at her. She leaned back in the old chair and rocked herself into a restless sleep. Dan's voice startled her awake.

"Emma. Good news! Charges were dropped and the conference approved my character."

Sweeping aside the cobwebs of sleep, she blurted, "Are we moving?"

"Yes. We're going to the Petroleum Circuit."

Emma asked, "Where is that?"

"Ritchie County, near the Ohio River in western West Virginia."

"I suppose they are even poorer than Grafton folks?" Emma asked.

Dan shrugged. "The churches are smaller. We'll find out in a couple of weeks. Poor or rich, they need the gospel."

"True words. Let's go inside, I'll fix us some coffee and we can talk more." She put her finger to her mouth and lowered her voice, "Johnny is asleep. We can give each other more attention if he stays that way."

When she brought the coffee and piece of berry pie to the table, he said softly, "I want to tell you about a wonderful man I met last Wednesday. Rev. James Robison is publisher of the Methodist Recorder."

"The paper from Pittsburg that you read every week?" she asked.

"That's the one!" Dan said.

"It's one of my favorites, too!"

"Rev. Robison told me the paper will have a new editor soon. His name is John Scott. I met Scott four years ago at the General Conference in Princeton, IL."

"How could I forget that," Emma quipped. "We had hardly been married a month when you left me for two weeks of meetings."

"I'm sorry, Honey. It really was an honor to represent southern Illinois."

She poured him another cup of coffee and asked, "Tell me about your visit with Robison. What's got you so worked up? Tell me quietly."

"We had a long talk about theology, philosophy, morality and the bible. I ended up giving him a copy of my pamphlet on baptism. He liked it and wants to see more of my writing."

Emma asked. "So, he wants you to send him articles for publication?"

"Yes. He told me he would put in a good word for me with the new editor. Sometimes they contract writers to do a series of articles. They pay an honorarium."

She smiled. "You know the way to this woman's heart."

Dan held up his empty pie plate, "And you know the way to this man's heart!"

Two weeks later, the Turneys traveled by train to Petroleum, West Virginia. Emma said, "It's the most desolate, remote place I've ever seen!"

Dan wasn't sure about the mountainous countryside, but felt welcomed by the stack of mail on the rickety table in their new parsonage. "Emma, it's a letter from *The Methodist Recorder!*" He tore it open and scanned the page. "Editor John Scott wants me to send a sample article!" Dan sorted through a satchel of his writings, searching for the right one to send to Scott.

Emma scolded, "Daniel Braxton, I need help unpacking these boxes and Johnny needs you more than Mr. Scott does." He apologized and swept Johnny into his arms. When dark came and Johnny slept, Turney was at the table writing to the editor. They exchanged letters. Dan's first submission was published. He sent more articles. Scott was impressed and wrote back, *"The Recorder* is considering an eight-week series on 'Moral Meditations.' Send us a column on how the truth of our Christian faith interacts with philosophy and modern science. We'd like a fresh take from a new voice. Please keep it under 1,000 words."

Emma read the letter. "That will be a challenge to squeeze all you know about truth, philosophy and science into a mere thousand words." While Dan struggled to limit his words, little Johnny began to use words. "Da-da!" "Momma!" From then on, the words gushed out. The toddler talked before he walked.

"Where does he get that?" Emma teased.

"Could be from either grandfather." Dan replied.

"Or directly from his own daddy!" Emma squeezed his hand.

Dan frowned. "I want to be a good father. Johnny's growing so fast. How are we going to feed and clothe him? Winter is upon us and the church wasn't able to pay me last month. Our pantry is bare."

"We will make do, Dan. The Lord will provide, you'll see. I'll pray, go finish tomorrow's sermon."

Before the ink was dry on his sermon, Dan heard a knock on the door.

"It's late. Were you expecting company?" Emma whispered. He shook his head and went to the door and welcomed the guests. Seven ladies and a young gentleman were loaded with clothing, dry goods and groceries.

"Petroleum wants you to feel welcomed, Rev. and Mrs. Turney. We hope these small gifts will help."

"What a blessing!" Emma said.

"It is more blessed to give, than to receive," their spokesperson replied. "Let me introduce our group." Dan forgot their names, but long remembered the United Presbyterian generosity.

When they left, Emma said, "Dan, our blessed Master provides!"

He shook his head. "Presbyterians! The Master is shaming his Methodist flock. I may have to add something to tomorrow's sermon."

Emma wanted to pray, but couldn't stop her practical self from calculating the store value of what they'd been given. She wanted to tell Dan it was $40 worth, but he was already adding to his sermon.

1880

Dan's tiny mountain churches struggled financially, but their pastor's mind was thriving. Ideas for his Methodist Recorder series exploded in his head. He delivered a few thought-provoking sermons to his meager crowds, but his heart wasn't in it. Turney's church folks picked up on his indifference. Small offerings got smaller. The church treasurers often told him, "We don't have the money to pay you this week." Emma was panicking, but Dan coped by writing. Sometimes the words gushed out like a snow-melt mountain stream. His first column flowed from his pen,

'The existence of God is a first truth. The idea of God is the most sublime conception which ever occupied the thought of man. Nothing equals it; nothing approximates it. In the whole range of thought, in the compass of truth, there is nothing in grandeur to compare with it. It is the noblest of all the conceptions of which the human mind is capable of... Everything else seems little and insignificant when compared to it. If truth is, God is; and if God is not, then truth does not exist."

When he was writing at full speed, Emma knew not to interrupt him. She kept the coffee coming and entertained Johnny. Dan was doing his second draft of the third column by the time editor Scott approved the first, "Fantastic. We couldn't be more pleased. Keep those meditations coming!"

Dan kept writing and kept neglecting his churches. Church members complained, "We don't want no professor, we just need a preacher." Long-buried quarrels among church members erupted.

"Em, what's happening?" Dan lamented.

"Neglected sheep turn into wolves," she quipped. He sat at the table, his face in his hands, his heart under conviction. On his 32nd birthday, April 17, Daniel wrote his new editor friend John Scott, begging for counsel.

Scott responded, "Rev. Turney, your intellectual gifts are too fine to be wasted on a mountainside in West Virginia. You need a bigger platform! There is an opening for a new Methodist Protestant Polemicist in Washington, D.C. With your permission, I want to suggest your name to the search committee. Your first column will be published this week and by summer, D.B. Turney will be a household name in M.P. circles. -Your friend, John Scott."

Scott's influence led to an interview for the D.C. position. Dan was offered the job. On Wednesday August 25, he traveled east to West Virginia's M.P. Annual Conference in Peel Tree. When he walked into the church, he wanted to shout out his fortune. But it was still a secret, as was Emma's pregnancy. Dan sought out conference president, G.W. Barrett, who complimented him on his meditations in the Recorder.

Dan confided to his supervisor, "I have been offered the D.C. Polemicist position and have accepted."

"That's good news!" Barrett said. "I am relieved. Objections have been raised against you and many would like to put you on the unstationed list."

"I won't even be offered a church?"

"That's right. The objections are strong, Daniel. They accuse you of attempting to do the work of a politician and the duties of a pastor at one and the same time...." Barrett waved off Dan's protests, "Critics think you are an injury and disgrace both to yourself and the Methodist Protestant Church. The polemicist position will be a better fit. Your D.C. job will let you be both pastor and politician."

The dreaded charges were brought against D.B. Turney. But presiding officer Barrett pacified the critics by suggesting that Turney transfer to another conference. One detractor muttered, "As long as he gets out of West Virginia."

Dan went back to Petroleum, relieved to be leaving West Virginia. Emma had started packing. "Wouldn't you know it. I'm pregnant and packing again. The last time I went back to Illinois to have our baby."

"Wouldn't it be an honor to have our baby born in Washington, D.C.?" he asked.

"Dan, I just want another healthy baby!"

"Me, too."

Emma asked, "Tell me again what you're going to do in D.C.?"

"I'll be the Polemicist, speaking out on behalf of the entire Methodist Protestant Church – researching and debating will be my job!"

"And preaching in D.C.?" she asked.

"Yes. A church will help feed us and the babies."

CHAPTER FIFTEEN

Washington D.C.
Fall 1880

Dan and Emma talked quietly, trying not to wake Johnny, who was squeezed into the seat beside his father. They couldn't afford three tickets and Emma didn't want a wiggly toddler sitting on her swelling tummy. Getting kicked from the inside was trouble enough. Dan squeezed her hand, "It will be all right. An apartment on East Capitol Street has been arranged for us. I meet church leaders tomorrow."

"So, you'll have to wait until Thursday to go to the Library of Congress?"

"Yes," he said, "but they have a table reserved for me." He was excited to be going to D.C. She was resigned. He had a church welcoming him and a new challenge speaking for the denomination. She had a child and another on the way. She dreaded big-city living and hated leaving her garden behind. Dan excitedly pointed out the window, "See those building! We're on the outskirts of D.C."

A few hours later, they were dropped off at 311 East Capitol. Dan lugged a suitcase up to their third-floor apartment. Johnny sniffed the smells in the hallway and reminded Emma of a hound dog they once had. They opened the door to a tiny furnished apartment. Johnny explored the three rooms under Emma's watchful eyes while Dan trudged downstairs for another load. On his third trip he told himself, 'You brought too many books!' Their belongings were stacked in a corner beside a wobbly dining room table. Johnny bounced on his little bed. Dan sat beside him and told one of Aesop's fables. "More!" Johnny cried. Two more fables and three bible stories later, Emma called them to the table. Supper was bread, cheese and the last carrots from Emma's garden She would cook turnips, greens and onions tomorrow. "At least the kitchen is furnished with a skillet and two pots," she said.

The morning sun woke Johnny and he woke his parents They'd slept the uneasy sleep of newcomers. Johnny rushed to the window, pushed aside the curtains and tapped on the glass. "Careful," Emma cautioned. After breakfast, Dan went down the hall and shaved before putting on his suit and tie. Emma straightened the tie, "You want to look your best, first impressions and all."

"Looks don't matter much," he said, "words do!"

"If words matter most," she said, "You'd the most handsome of men."

He kissed her. "I don't know when I'll be home."

"We'll be here, though Johnny and I may go out and look for a grocer."

Dan took a trolley car to the 9th Street Methodist Protestant Church. He was welcomed by James York. "Rev. Turney, our congregation has been blessed to have some of the best preachers in the country. A Polemicist for the entire denomination has to be a talker and a thinker too. York offered, "Let me show you the sanctuary!" He led Dan to a door behind the pulpit. The door opened into the preacher's study which doubled as an all-purpose room. The space was jammed with a desk, two chairs, old candles and a vase with withered flowers. Behind the desk was a cupboard of communion trays and a bookshelf.

Dan scanned the assortment of books previous pastors left behind and picked up the *1870 M.P. Book of Discipline*. Flipping through the pages, he couldn't resist commenting, "We Methodist

Protestants try to chart our own way, but often end up looking like Methodist Episcopalians."

York replied, "Don't I know it. My granddad was one of the rebels who broke away in 1830. This congregation started not long after that."

"My granddad stayed with the M.E.s," Dan said. "I was the one who broke off and became an M.P. Or, you could say I was booted out. I couldn't get used to the bishop's bit in my mouth."

"That's good," York said. "We don't have bishops, not even here in the capital. But we have senators, congressmen and justices to make up for the missing bishops. You can make a mess if you mix too much religion with even a little politics. Your predecessor went too far stirring that pot!"

"Doing what?" Dan asked.

"Wouldn't be for me to judge; just offering some friendly advice."

"Could I ask a personal question, James?" Dan said. "My wife, Emma, is expecting and we need to find a doctor. Can you suggest one?"

York said, "I can do that. Dr. George Gross is a member of our church. I'll introduce you to him on Sunday. He's always in church, unless he gets called away by an emergency."

On Sunday, after services, York introduced Dan and Emma to Dr. Gross. Emma found him easy to talk to and ended up telling him about losing two babies in the same week. Dr. Gross said, "The Lord willing, we'll deliver your new little one safe and sound!"

1881

Two months later, the doctor was at the Turney's apartment helping deliver their baby. "It's a boy!" Gross announced. Emma cried tears of relief and gratitude, but now faced a dilemma. She had avoided talking with Dan about names. She didn't want him to suggest another strange Greek name like he did for their stillborn, Metta.

Dan told her, "I've been thinking about a name. I'd like us to name him George. George Joseph Turney."

Emma liked the name, but asked, "Why George? We don't have Georges in our families."

"We will now," Dan said. I want to name him after Rev. George Roork. He brought me to the Lord back in Oregon. He's one of the finest Christian men I've known."

Doctor George Gross, who was in the kitchen cleaning up, interrupted, "And here I thought you were naming little George after me!"

"That, too!" Dan smiled as patted his son's hand, "George Joseph, I hope you get to meet George Roork!"

Emma recovered quickly and found a daily rhythm of nursing baby George and listening to talkative Johnny. Dan enjoyed his rhythm of weekly preaching, study in the Library of Congress and writing letters. But he struggled to make personal connections with senators and congressmen. In late February, he wrote his father about this dilemma. Ten days later, he read L. Jay S. Turney's reply, "…We are deeply anxious for your success and I am willing to do anything in my power to secure your desires and promote your interests." His father listed several names and included some sage advice, "Get acquainted with all the leading Senators and Congressmen you can. Treat all politely, get into debates with none… and when opportunity offers ask each for his influence…."

Dan made an appointment with the first person listed in his father's letter, Illinois Senator John A. Logan. "Sir, thank you for seeing me."

"Glad to meet you, Rev. Turney. I just got your father's letter. He and I have both done some political side-switching. I also knew your grandfather, Braxton Parish. A fine man! But my favorite in your family was your uncle Judge William K. Parish. We were best friends. Did you know he officiated at our wedding and we honeymooned in his home?"

"No, I didn't." Dan admitted. "Uncle William died just before we went west to the Washington Territory."

Logan said, "Guess we were both at his funeral. It was a sad day. Nothing hurts like the death of your closest friend. The War began and death became our constant companion. Were you too young to fight in the War?"

"I was, but it was a noble cause," Dan said.

"We paid with blood for our freedom and the end of slavery's curse. Slavery is over, but reconstruction isn't finished...." Logan threw up his hands. "Sorry to sound like I'm on the campaign stump! How can I help you, Rev. Turney?"

Dan explained his role as Methodist Protestant Polemicist.

"What issues do you M.P.s especially care about?" Logan asked.

"Senator, we want people to have faith in the Lord Jesus and follow him!"

Logan nodded, "Sounds like the Methodists I've known through the years!"

"For me, personally," Dan continued, "I have a heart for both suffrage and prohibition!"

"My wife would agree with you on both. I'm not a drinker and think the day will come when women get the vote. Not sure we're ready yet," Logan added.

"Not ready or not willing?" Dan blurted out. Logan stiffened.

"That's OK, son. Change isn't easy to stomach. But some changes are worth fighting for. You fight for what you think is right. Be a good soldier for your causes!" Logan stood and offered his hand.

"Thank you, Senator Logan," Dan said.

As he turned to leave, Logan offered, "Preacher, maybe I can offer some immediate help. Would you like to hobnob with congressmen and maybe meet President Garfield?"

"Yes sir!"

"Thursday, my wife and I have been invited to the Executive Mansion to meet the Garfields. I'd be honored to have you and Mrs. Turney join us if you're able. All of Washington's top brass will be there!"

Dan shook his hand, "Thank you, sir!"

There was a bounce in his steps as Dan hurried home, eager to tell Emma the news. "I'm happy for you Dan. But will my Sunday dress be spiffy enough for such an auspicious occasion?"

"Your smile makes that dress spiffy enough to suit me!"

Three days later, they walked to the White House, jammed full of dignitaries, politicians, lobbyists, job-seekers and ordinary citizens. When the crowd funneled into an entryway, Dan caught the eye of an officer who was screening the pressing crowd. "Sir, we're guests of Senator Logan."

Dan and Emma were ushered into the lobby. He stood on tiptoes, searching the crowd for Logan and waved when he spotted the senator. Logan motioned them over.

"Rev. and Mrs. Turney, this is my wife Mary. They are actually having two receptions today- one for President Garfield and one for Mrs. Garfield. Mrs. Turney, my wife will take you to the reception for Mrs. Garfield. The crowd is smaller. Dan, I'm afraid I have a command performance. I need to go in with the Illinois delegation. Hopefully, they'll let you come in after the dignitaries are received. Sorry." Logan rushed off and his wife took Emma by the arm and ushered her to Mrs. Garfield's reception. Dan was left standing in a crowd of strangers. Then he saw a familiar face and pushed his way through the crowd,

"Mr. Farley," Dan waved.

"Rev. Turney! What brings you here? Haven't seen you since Edgar County. You got married, then skedaddled."

Dan shook the editor's hand. "I live just a few blocks away. I preach over at the 9th Street M.P. church."

"I'll be in D.C. for a few days. I might just show up on Sunday. You're a rare preacher. You write as well as you speak." Dan was telling him about Johnny and baby George, when Farley's group was invited to greet the president. Memories of his first years of preaching flooded Turney's mind as he watched the editor step into the line. Dan waited, but his turn never came. Eventually Emma and Mrs. Logan found him. She apologized, "Rev. Turney, we're sorry you didn't get to greet the president. Many people were turned away and Garfield had to leave for important meetings."

Emma exclaimed, "I am so delighted to have met Mrs. Garfield. Thank you for letting me tag along. It's getting late, we need to go home to the boys."

On the short walk back to their apartment, Emma said, "I can't find a word fancy enough to describe that party- elegant, resplendent, sumptuous! I felt way out of my element." Dan felt left out, an outsider with no way in.

Busy congressmen were not interested in Turney's intellectual and philosophical ramblings. He'd engaged one senator on women's suffrage and was rebuffed with, "Women should know their place and stay there." Dan complained to Emma. She held a crying baby with one arm and pan of beans in the other, "Don't expect sympathy from me. I'm not sure you men will ever let us vote! But I'll let you hold baby George for a spell. He has a bellyache today."

Dan carried his son to his desk, cuddled him with his left arm and wrote with his right. It was a letter to a southern congressman. Later he'd discover that the Kentucky politician loved his liquor and his constituents would not tolerate prohibition.

In April, cherry blossoms and circumstances improved Dan's mood. He found an ardent suffrage supporter in Massachusetts Senator George Hoar, who confided, "Next year I'm going to push for a select committee on women's suffrage." Turney encouraged the senator and felt better about his work. The legislative session drew to a close on May 20. Senators, congressmen, and staffers scrambled to railroad stations to catch trains home.

Emma said, "I am jealous. They get to go home."

"Your heart is always in Illinois, isn't it!"

"Yes, it is! Dan, did you hear a knock on the door?"

He pushed back his chair and went to the door. A messenger greeted him.

"Rev. D.B. Turney? A telegram for you, sir."

Emma reminded Dan to tip the delivery boy.

"What could this be?" he asked as he tore the envelope open.

The message jolted him. He staggered back to his chair. He collapsed, wadding the telegram into a yellow ball.

"Dan, what is it?" Emma hurried across the room.

He looked up. "It's Dad. He died this morning. Here we are in Washington, D.C., the place dad always wanted to come to."

"And we can't be in Benton with your mother," Emma finished his thought.

"My brother John is out west practicing medicine. Margaret is gone and Leander is not grown up yet. It's a good thing Mom's brother Tom is still in Benton"

Emma said, "Elizabeth Turney is a strong woman."

"She had to be. She was married to my dad!"

A week later, they got a comforting letter from the Benton M.E. church pastor, "L. Jay S. Turney died in the triumph of faith!"

Dan cried and Emma consoled him, "That old reprobate came around to faith in the end!"

"Not any too soon!" Dan blubbered. Johnny stood like a soldier beside his father's chair and patted Dan's knee.

On July 2nd tragedy struck the nation-- an assassin shot President James Garfield in the Potomac Railroad Station. Lawyer Charles Guiteau shot him because he felt Garfield owed him a political appointment. Dan sat at his table in the Library and reflected on life and death, 'Ambition. Pride, Arrogance! We are indeed a fallen race!' As President Garfield lay dying, Dan felt his own polemics passion draining from his soul.

That night, he confessed, "Em, my passion for this work has cooled. I have done what I could. Maybe it's time...."

"Time to go back to Illinois?" she asked.

"Yes. I'll write the conference back home and see if they can find a place for us, I need to talk with Mr. York and Dr. Gross, at 9th Street Church." Two weeks later, Dan got a letter from Methodist Protestant leaders in Illinois, assuring him of an appointment. Emma wanted to go home, but when she counted the coins in her saving's jar, she lamented, "We don't have enough to buy the train tickets!"

Dan said, "I'll ask the church to take up a collection for us." The 9th Street M.P. church offering paid for their fare. Emma hid her savings for another day and started packing. Just as they were ready to go leave the apartment for the train depot, Dan got another telegram. It was good news. "D.B. Turney, you are invited to deliver the opening sermon at the S. Ill. M.P. 1881 Annual Conference."

105

CHAPTER SIXTEEN

Lawrence Co., Illinois
Fall 1881

The Turneys barely caught their train back to Illinois. The swaying train soon rocked the boys to sleep. Emma nodded off and finally Dan fell asleep. He dreamt he was walking up the steps onto a big stage. A deep voice boomed, "Rev. Daniel Braxton Turney, you have been elected president of the conference."

Two weeks later, that dream came true. His electrifying sermon on the first day of conference brought people to their feet. When it came time to elect officers for the Southern Illinois Methodist Protestant Conference, Dan was nominated and elected unanimously as president. He would visit churches in southern Illinois, preside over the next conference session and receive a small stipend. His church assignment was the circuit in Lawrence County, just 30 miles north of his hometown of Fairfield. He would serve five churches scattered over half the county.

A lay person gave them a tour of the parsonage, "Widow Hinde gave the house to the church, in her will. We got it cleaned up. Rev. Feltz left a bit of a mess behind when he took a church over in Indiana."

"Guess, he didn't go far?" Dan said.

"No siree! You can see Indiana from your porch."

Dan and Emma Turney spent a year in Lawrenceville. Dan preached three times on Sunday and again on Thursday nights. He visited conference churches, whenever he could. They had barely settled in when he got a letter from Ada Kepley inviting him to speak at a W.C.T.U. rally in Effingham, "Alcohol is to blame for many of society's problems, including severe health problems, poverty and crime. Our slogan is *Moderation in all things healthful; total abstinence from all things harmful.* We are planning a joint rally with The Anti-Saloon League and want you to be our keynote speaker. We will reimburse your travel expenses and pay a small honorarium. The rally will be at the Old Southern Methodist Church in Effingham." Dan gladly accepted her offer.

1882

The Effingham rally spread the word that D.B. Turney was a rising star in the temperance movement in Illinois. The Bloomington Bulletin reported that Dan persuaded the state temperance convention to urge local prohibition of the liquor traffic, the adoption of equal suffrage and other needed reforms. Prohibition leaders in eastern Illinois encouraged him to run for congress, "The Mt. Carmel District needs your voice!" Dan threw his hat in the ring. Some ridiculed him. The Mt. Carmel Register called him the *whangdoodle* candidate. Dan had the announcement of his candidacy printed on strips of cloth, which he nailed up at crossroads on trees and stumps throughout the district. But his efforts were in vain. He lost in a lopsided election. He also lost favor with leaders in the Southern Illinois M.P. Conference who felt neglected, "D.B. Turney is more prohibitionist than president! More politician than preacher!"

Dan could see the handwriting on the wall and was relieved when a prominent Methodist Protestant leader from the North Illinois Conference invited him to come up north to preach in the Bloomington Circuit. Emma agreed to move.

CHAPTER SEVENTEEN

Northern Illinois
Nov. 1882

On Wednesday, November 22, they moved into the parsonage in Old Town near Bloomington's Pleasant Grove Church. They ate thanksgiving dinner in their new home. Thanks to the generosity of church members and neighbors, it was a feast. When the boys were asleep, Emma threw her arms around Dan's neck, "It's so good to be here!"

"We'll make good memories, here!" Dan predicted.

Emma would never forget the noisy hubbub of five-year-old Johnny chasing his little brother George through the big house. She wished Dan was in the room whenever Johnny went into questioning mode, "Why?" "What is this?" "Why does Daddy close the study door?"

"Because you boys make so much racket!" Emma answered. John accused, "It's George's fault!" Little George got that look on his face as he said, "No. George not do!" A knock on the door ended their little spat. A messenger handed Emma a telegram.

"Dan," she yelled as she rushed to the study door. The door burst open and almost knocked her down. "It's your mother. She can't take care of herself any longer!"

1883

Dan took the train south to Benton, Illinois. Elizabeth Turney was so frail. He asked his uncle Tom Parish, "How can she be so weak? She's not sixty yet?" Tom had no answer. They had to carry her from the bench to the train steps. He tried to talk with her on the way back to Bloomington, but she kept falling asleep. Daniel gave up and opened a book.

Elizabeth Turney's declining health threw a pall over the Turney household. The boy's voices were muted and they avoided the room where she lay. Dan tried to coax his mother into talking, but often settled for reading to her. Emma was burdened with the added responsibilities of caring for her weakening mother-in-law. Elizabeth Parish Turney died April 27, 1883 in Old Town township. Not having the money to send her back to Benton to be buried beside L. Jay S. Turney, they buried her in the little cemetery behind the church. They couldn't afford a headstone. Grass soon hid her gravesite, which was framed by Sendele, Shrigley and Rodman head stones. Normal life eventually returned to the parsonage.

One summer morning, Dan announced. "We need an outing. Let's dress up and have a family picture taken!" Emma resisted until Dan explained, "We should have gotten a family photo before Mom died. I want one taken now, even if you are pregnant."

Johnny asked, "What does pregnant mean?" Emma ignored the question and whispered to Dan, "I don't mean to be superstitious, but we always end up moving when I'm expecting."

Johnny asked, "What's expecting?"

"Boys, get on your fancy duds, we're going to Saybrook to get our picture taken!"

Dan was right about the family photo and Emma was right about moving. They moved to LaHarpe in Hancock County, Illinois early that fall. Margaret Virginia Turney was born on November 2. While Emma nursed her newborn, Dan told her, "I just as well transfer to the Northern Illinois Conference. I'm going to ask for a year of study leave."

"How will we survive?" Emma asked.

1884

"I can still preach here in LaHarpe." The paper-work was slow in getting through and before D.B. Turney was transferred, the powers-that-be decided he should represent the Southern Illinois Conference at The Methodist Protestant National Convention in Baltimore, Maryland.

Dan was excited to go. The convention would be in the heart of Methodist Protestant country. Emma warned, "Don't you get asked to go back east and preach!" He shrugged, but she wasn't finished, "And don't go making speeches that make headlines. You know what I mean!"

In late May, Emma sat in her favorite chair and opened the newspaper. She eagerly looked for news about the Methodist Protestant Convention in Maryland. She had enjoyed earlier articles about plans to celebrate Methodism's 1884 centennial and possible mergers with kindred denominations. 'What will I find today?' she asked herself as she turned to the fourth page. Her eyes focused on the first sentence, "At the Methodist Protestant Convention today Rev. D.B. Turney, of Southern Illinois, presented a protest against the action of yesterday on the restriction of the rule regarding the time of pastors."

Emma cried out, "Daniel, Daniel Braxton Turney, couldn't you have kept quiet for once! I don't even understand what you were protesting, but I know you resist restrictions."

Johnny called out from the other room, "Mom, are you OK?"

Emma left the crumpled newspaper and her irritation while she gave her oldest some attention. "Sh...sh. Don't wake George and baby Margaret."

Dan returned from the pomp and splendor of Maryland's convention to the routine and demands of family and church. He discovered that a leading parishioner had just died. Dan pulled on his jacket and apologized, "I have to go see widow Jones." Emma understood. Her father used to say, "Death is no respecter of persons or preachers. When it calls, we go." After the funeral, D.B. Turney got the news that he would not be nominated by the republicans for congress in the 11th district. Both W.H. Gest and Robert Moir got more votes. Dan admitted, "I best focus on church work and stay out of the spotlight

1885-1886

They moved from LaHarpe to the tiny village of New Bedford in Bureau County. In February of 1886, they traded the isolated hamlet for a new church start in the growing mining community of Spring Valley in LaSalle County. The town was only two years old, but had exploded to more than 2,000 in population. The growth was so rapid that some called it 'The Magic City.' Emma teased Dan about working his preaching magic in this new place. He retorted, "You know I don't believe in magic!"

"But you do believe in supernatural spiritual power! Rev. Turney, I have read your pamphlets and heard you preach!"

Dan needed all the power he could muster. Starting a new congregation in a bustling mining town was no easy task. M.P. leaders thought he would be a good fit; he could draw a crowd and had experience preaching to miners in West Virginia. The new church was to be planted in Spring Valley, but housing was so sparse that the Turneys had to live in neighboring Peru. In addition to the start-up church, Dan served Farm Ridge, a country church in the next county.

On August 5th, Dan got back in the political spotlight when the Prohibition Convention nominated him as their candidate for the 8th congressional district. Emma warned, "Don't let this go to your head!" But he was infected again. He liked hearing people say, "You ought to be the party's nominee for the vice-presidency."

A letter from his baby brother, Leander, brought him back to reality. "Brother Dan, I feel called to follow in your steps and preach. I have been accepted by a school in Chicago."

"That's not far from here!" Emma exclaimed.

Dan read the rest of the letter. "He's looking to find a church where he can preach." An idea popped into his head. "What if I had

111

him preach for me over in Farm Ridge? I could school him in preaching, while he goes to school! Rail service to Chicago is good."

Emma caught his enthusiasm. "He could live with us on weekends. This big old house has a back room that's all but empty!"

The wheels were rolling. Dan contacted the M.P. stationing committee. The church needed young blood and Leander was 20 years young. Letters were exchanged and by mid-September, the deal was done. The North IL M.P. Conference made it official and Leander Turney was appointed to preach at Farm Ridge. He moved into the back room. Like his big brother, Leander brought more books than clothes. He opened his suitcase and lifted out a package. He carefully opened it, then waved it in Dan's face. "My chess set! I'm as good at chess as you are at shooting a gun. I challenge you to a match!"

Before they could open the chess board, John and George were climbing all over Leander. They gave him an eager welcome into the family. The chess game didn't happen for weeks.

Dan went with Leander on his first Sunday, introduced him to the Farm Ridge congregation and sat on the pew to listen to his brother's first sermon. Leander was nervous, but did well enough. On the way home, Leander asked for an evaluation and Dan gave a frank critique. Leander smiled. "I promise to be as kind to you after our first chess match." Dan smiled. He couldn't imagine losing to his baby brother. But no matter how hard he tried, he never beat his baby brother in chess. It was no consolation that Leander was being recognized as one of Chicago's best young chess masters.

Every weekend, Leander would re-enter the family. He'd do tricks and wrestle with the children; then he and Dan would wrestle with biblical doctrines and theology. Leander was an eager, curious student who enjoyed disagreeing with teachers and with his brother.

One Sunday afternoon, when the children were down for their nap, Emma heard Leander and Dan going at it again. She shook her head. Leander dared to disagree with Dan about baptism. She chimed in, "Careful Leander, Dan is as passionate about infant baptism as you are about chess."

"Emma, is right about that, as she is about most things." Dan said. "Leander, I have something I want to give you." He handed his brother a small package.

"What is this?" Leander asked.

"It's a draft of my latest booklet, *The Mode of Baptism*. I'd like to know what you think of it."

Leander said, "I'll be glad to read it, but you know I'm leaning more toward baptist views on the subject."

"Just don't lean over too far and fall into the deep water," Dan quipped.

Leander was about to argue, when both Johnny and George jumped into his lap.

1887-1888

Daniel and Leander had many discussions that winter about baptism.

"Emma, I'm losing him!" Dan exclaimed one night.

"What do you mean?"

"My brother Leander, not only disagrees with me, he disagrees with all Methodists. He's headed for the Baptist road."

"That leaves a sour taste on your tongue?"

"It does!" Dan lamented. "But he still feels called to preach. Baptist preachers aren't all bad; they're just wrong about baptism!"

"Which is why you're a Methodist!" Emma said.

"One of the reasons," he answered. "I'm going to rework my baptism pamphlet."

"When you perfect it, let me read it!"

Dan's baptism pamphlet went better than his church work. His efforts to start a new Methodist Protestant congregation in Spring Valley were in vain. In August, the prohibition party congressional convention nominated him for the 8th district. Election posters proclaimed, "If every prohibitionist does his duty, Daniel B. Turney will be elected." Either the party misjudged their numbers or they failed to turn out to vote. He lost another election.

Emma asked, "Don't you ever feel like giving up on your pet causes?"

"Emma, truth is not determined by elections, but by reason and scripture."

"You still going on that speaking tour?"

"I am! I go to Foosland in early March for a baptismal debate and then to Michigan to make several prohibition speeches."

Emma's voice broke, "Dan, your children will grow up and be gone from home while you're off speaking somewhere!"

"I'm sorry, Em. It's who I am!"

They hugged, both hoping to heal the distance growing between them.

She patted him on the back, "Rev. Turney, do what you must do and say what you must say. I try to understand, but I don't have to like it!"

Some area newspapers couldn't accept D. B. Turney's passions, were suspicious of his motives and thought he was a 'crank' who ought to be suppressed. But Dan pressed on. That fall he published *The Mode of Baptism*, sending his first copy to his brother Leander. It gave him an odd sense of satisfaction, but he doubted it would change his brother's mind. His booklet got little publicity, but an act of generosity by Dan made news in the *Springfield Daily Register*.

When Emma saw the article, she chided, "Dan, I respect your generosity to widow Morrison, but we're too poor for you to be giving her so much money! Two-hundred dollars? We're barely making ends meet, as it is."

Dan didn't feel like apologizing for a kind deed and walked toward his study. "Don't you ignore me, Rev. Turney!" she exclaimed. "God gave you a generous heart, I can't deny that. But God seems to have given me the good sense in this family. Go take a long look at your sleeping children. They are not hungry, but they barely have enough to eat. Their clothes are all patched up and they need new shoes!"

He was shamed into walking into the bedroom where the children slept. John, almost nine, shared a small bed with six-year-old George. Four-year-old Maggie was snuggled in across the room. Dan tiptoed to the boys' bed and pulled up the old blanket they slept under. Both stirred. Dan retreated to the doorway where Emma stood. She was touched by this rare scene. "Dan, you're not wrong to give to others. Just don't forget the needs of your own children."

"You're right Em. You have more common sense in your little finger than I have in my whole body. You hold our family together!" Dan vowed to spend more time with the children. Emma didn't doubt his intentions, but wasn't sure much would change. He established a pattern of reading to the boys at night or having them read to him. They thrived under his attention.

But that new habit was lost in September 1887, when D. B. Turney was appointed to the Lincoln and Natrona Circuits in Logan County, Illinois. John and George hugged their uncle's legs when they said goodbye to Leander. "Why can't he come with us?" They moved 90 miles south and Leander went back to school in Chicago. Everyone in the family, except Dan felt uprooted. His political reputation was growing. A Wichita Kansas newspaper supported him for the vice presidency on the prohibition ticket, "If Turney keeps on saying good things he will be there. He... said that 'local option is too local and too optional.' He has a way of saying things that fit very nicely with the times."

His political fame was rising, his church ministry was failing. The Lincoln-Natrona Circuit proved too big for one preacher. The church stationing committee saw what was happening and that fall the circuit was broken up; Lincoln was given a new pastor, Natrona was left without a pastor, D.B. Turney continued temporarily. Once overworked, now he felt underutilized.

1889

Dan received some recognition by being named 'Conference Missionary.' Emma asked, "How much do you get paid?"

"There's no set salary, but I'll get a small portion of whatever churches give to the president's fund," he admitted.

She held up her right little finger. "Remember what you said about my common sense?"

"I do!" he replied. "It's still true."

"Maybe it's time to look for a better appointment, even if we have to move to another conference or state!"

Yielding to her judgment, he said, "I'll write some letters."

While they waited for answers, Turney was not idle. He continued speaking out for prohibition. One night he lectured to a rather noisy crowd. Some waved beer bottles, others threw rotten eggs or green apples. Shouters interrupted his opening. Dan raised his voice, "Now gentlemen, how many of you would like a good blackguard story? All in favor, raise your hand." A majority immediately raised their hands. Dan launched into his usual talking points. Before he could finish, a disgruntled listener, sick of Dan's prohibition logic, shouted, "Where's that story?"

"My dear sir," Dan replied, "I did not promise to tell you any such story. Of course not. I merely wished to know how many blackguards were here. You held up your hand."

The victim of Dan's wit, remarked, "I don't see why they call you the Abe Lincoln of the Prohibs; you never told us one blamed story in your hifalutin speech!" Another rabble rouser chimed in, "Turney is the Abe Lincoln of the Prohibition Party because Lincoln was a homely man and we can all see that Mr. Turney is also very homely!" The crowd roared. Dan smiled.

After the meeting, one of Dan's supporters said, "You handled those scoundrels well! Did you read how George Dahoney likened you to Abe? You are the apostle of prohibition who will do for prohibition in 1892 what Abraham Lincoln did for republicans in 1860!"

When Dan got home, Emma met him with a hard question, "Did you take a collection, or did you get paid?"

Dan smiled, "I got a few rotten eggs and green apples, but I left them there.

"I'm serious, Dan!" He sat down, sipped the coffee she had poured and listened as she poured out her concerns. "I hope you hear from a church soon, or we'll have to cook up those rotten eggs and green apples!"

CHAPTER EIGHTEEN

Bennett, Iowa
Dec. 1889

Emma's prayers were answered when he was invited to serve in Bennett, Iowa. They packed up in December and headed for eastern Iowa. When they crossed the Mississippi River at Rock Island, Johnny announced, "We're in Iowa, now!"

A drowsy Maggie asked, "How much further?"

Emma gave her a hug, "We're most of the way there."

They rode through an undulating sea of rolling farmland before reaching the growing town of Bennett, just 35 miles from the river. Emma was glad a parsonage waited for them. "Dan, imagine how hard it would be if we had to look for a house every time we moved?"

Johnny asked, "Dad, is this where you'll preach?"

"Yes. Here in Bennett, over in Tipton and also in two country churches called Hebron Chapel and Virginia Grove."

"Why do they call it Virginia? Isn't that a state?" eight-year-old George asked.

"I don't know?" his father admitted. "We'll have to ask."

George had to wait two weeks for an answer. The Turneys traveled through a snowstorm to get to Virginia Grove. The church folks welcomed them with a big fire in the woodstove. It was so hot close to the stove that George unbuttoned his coat before asking about the name. John Bolton, patted George on the head, "Good question. David McCroskey named the church back in 1862. Virginia was his home state and he was a big land owner in these parts; but it was George Smith who gave the land for the church, school and cemetery."

George said, "I was born in Washington, D.C."

Bolton said, "D.C.'s right next to Virginia, too bad I can't introduce you to Mr. McCrosky."

"Why not?" George asked.

Bolton pointed out the window, "McCrosky's in that cemetery across the road."

George walked across the plank floor and stared out through the frosty window. "Which stone is his?"

"The big one next to the oak tree."

Dan interrupted the history lesson, "Time to get this Quarterly Conference started. Could someone lead us in a hymn sing?"

"We're Methodists aren't we!" Bolton said as he picked up a hymnal and motioned for people to join him.

1890

That winter, Dan discovered that folks in all four churches liked to sing. He told Emma, "I think they'd rather sing than listen to me preach."

"If you shortened your sermons, they could sing longer," she teased. He didn't smile, so Emma added, "But as far as I am concerned, you could have preached for another hour about "The Balm and the Physician!"

"I love that text from Jeremiah 8:22," he smiled.

"There is a balm in Gilead," she quoted.

"I hope there is also balm in Hebron, Iowa!" Daniel quipped.

"If not, we'll have to let our healing light shine!"

Spring sunshine broke through winter's gloom and spotlighted the shabby condition of the Bennett church building's outside walls. Dan complained to the trustees. An old codger responded, "Why don't you paint it Reverend? It would do you good to have a paint brush in your hand instead of a coffee cup." Dan's blood was boiling as he recruited a bunch of men to paint the church. He even enlisted his boys. "John, get your brother George. You two are big enough to help paint."

"I can climb a ladder," John bragged. "But George is too little."

Dan said, "Boys, I want you both painting down low. No ladders yet. I'll stay and help you. They watched the church men climb the ladders. Dan showed the boys how to brush on the paint. They coated the whole building with a fresh coat of white paint before the day was over. "That will show that old trustee curmudgeon," Dan muttered. His troubles with trustees were just starting.

One parishioner loved his style and told him, "Rev. Turney, a minister should take a firm stand and speak his mind!" Emma winced and later warned him that not everyone agreed with that sentiment. Within a week, Dan had a run-in with a temperance lecturer and refused to let him speak in the M.P. church. Emma chided, "Wouldn't he have helped our prohibition cause?" Emma had just become treasurer of a local group promoting the prohibitory amendment in Nebraska. Dan's answer didn't settle her question. Building use surfaced again when a church trustee wanted to let a Masonic group use the church free of charge. Dan said, "We ought to charge them 75 cents per night!" He refused to give up his keys to open the building.

D.B. Turney was excited to have his Prohibition Party letter published in the *Chicago News*. A town gossip spread the word, "Rev. Turney claims no democrat or republican can be a true prohibitionist." That fire was fueled when the state prohibition party nominated Daniel Turney for court justice. Dan's keynote convention speech was described as "a diatribe against the Republican party." The election campaign was unsuccessful and Dan's critics ridiculed the pathetic voter turn-out. Dan shrugged it off and by Saturday was back on the speaking trail. He was in a buggy borrowed from the Methodist Episcopal minister Rev. Mitchell of Tipton. J.E. Cook was driving him to nearby Rochester. They were in a hurry to make it to a special Saturday night service. Rounding the curve near Plato, a deer darted in front of them.

The horse spooked and Cook lost control. The right wheel hit a culvert and plunged them into a deep ditch.

Dan woke, with Emma wiping his face with a wet cloth. She could see his bewilderment. "Dan, you were in a buggy wreck. The doctor thinks you may have broken your collar bone and have dislocated a rib." He touched his aching forehead. "You also have an ugly gash on your head. The doctor stitched you up. Your driver, Mr. Cook, just got some bruises. But the buggy was totally wrecked."

"I can't remember anything," Dan said.

"Church folks will help out, until you can get back on your feet."

"I have to work on my sermon!" he said. But when he tried to sit up, pain shot through his shoulder and he quickly laid back down.

Johnny, George and Maggie tiptoed into the room, but Emma shooed them away, "Your father will be fine, but he has to rest."

His recovery was quick. Confined to bed, Emma brought him books to read. After school, the boys read to him. Maggie couldn't keep up with them. Emma watched from the doorway, knowing these precious moments would be gone all too soon. Within a week, Dan was back at his desk writing sermons and thanking God that he hadn't injured his right shoulder. He worried a bit about the scar on his forehead, but then remembered some folks already considered him as homely as Lincoln. Emma consoled him, "The scar gives your face more character." Her comment inspired a sermon illustration which he hurriedly wrote down.

He started preaching again and found himself back in the Cedar County spotlight. An anonymous Bennett resident, calling himself *'Evening Star',* wrote a letter to the Tipton newspaper attacking Turney and questioning his temperance, "He drinks up to seven cups of coffee at a meal. He's the biggest drinker in Cedar County!"

Dan clenched his fists, "I never drink more than three cups!" Emma smiled. "Listen to what else Mr. Star wrote, "The church in Bennett is enjoying a new coat of paint and anticipating the absence of Daniel B. Turney." Dan stormed over to the newspaper office and complained. They refused to release the letter writer's name. Dan went to the county attorney in Tipton, "Can't you find out who this writer is? I'll sue him for defamation of character!"

"Calm down, Rev. Turney, this person has the constitutional right to free speech, just as you do."

Dan jumped to his feet, "Anonymity shouldn't give him the freedom to insult my good name!"

The attorney tried to lighten the situation, "Would you care for a cup of coffee before you go?"

Dan got the joke, but didn't laugh. He stomped out of the office. By the time he got back to Bennett, he wished he had accepted the coffee. Emma was limiting the amount of coffee they could buy. "Dan, we can't pay our bills and the churches are behind on your salary."

Dan apologized, "There's a financial plague on the Methodist Protestant House. Our churches are all small and they're all struggling."

Unpaid bills distressed the Bennett M.P. church. A $500 lien was placed against the church for failing to pay its' bills. Dan went to the court house to plead the church's case, but got no sympathy. In September, he pled with the Annual Conference for relief. "The church's property might be sold to pay the debt. Can the Iowa Conference afford the loss of such a valuable asset?" They listened to his lament, but had no funds to bail out a debt-ridden church. The stationing committee decided the best answer was to replace Turney with a more financial savvy preacher. Rev. Roland Moulton took over the Tipton Circuit and held a revival that raised enough money to pay off the debt within three months.

CHAPTER NINETEEN

Central Iowa
1891

Daniel B. Turney and his family moved to Spring Hill and Wheeling in central Iowa.

He'd been assigned to the 18 member Wheeling church in Marion County. They were to live in an abandoned, but fixed-up parsonage in Spring Hill, 25 miles west in Warren County. Emma asked, "Dan, how can we live on $250 a year?"

"We'll find a way. Folks in Spring Hill hope we can get their church going again."

Emma wondered aloud, "How did they end up with a parsonage and no congregation?"

"They once shared the building with the Baptists," he said.

Johnny asked, "Aren't they the ones who baptize by dunking adults?"

"They are," Dan said.

Emma chided, "So you'll preach your baptism sermon every week, until the Baptists start bringing their babies to be sprinkled!" Johnny laughed. Dan smiled, but secretly feared it might not work. "What other choice do I have?" he mumbled to himself. The house in Spring Hill smelled of fresh paint. George cried out, "Look at these food baskets!"

The people hoped and Dan tried, but his fears bore more fruit than their hopes. The church in Spring Hill did not get started again and he had only one baptism to show for his work at Wheeling. It was time to move again.

1892

They moved north to the Edenville Circuit in Marshall County. John, now a teenager, enjoyed asking snarky questions, "Isn't Eden the circuit Adam and Eve served?" Emma ignored him, but Dan gave him 'the look.' Eleven-year-old George kept his mouth shut and Maggie was too young to enter in, except to say, "I hope I'll find friends there. Will we live in Eden?"

Emma said, "Today they call the town Rhodes. That's where we'll live and we'll all find new friends."

"Will we be in school together?"

"Yes," Emma said, "at least until John goes to high school."

1893-1894

Shortly after they moved, Dan added St. Anthony's to his preaching circuit. Dan was having trouble keeping up with his sons. Johnny was an instigator and George followed. One night, Johnny was on a tear and told his parents at supper, "Dad, you showed us a copy of a newspaper you printed out in Oregon when you were a teenager."

"I was twenty!"

"George and I want to be printers!"

Dan asked, "Printing sale bills?"

"We'll start small, call it *Turney Brothers' Printing Company*," he said, winking at George.

Emma asked, "I suppose you'll need to buy a printing press?"

Johnny nodded, "That's what we want to do. George and I can work and save the money to buy a press."

"Do you know how much a small press would cost?" Emma and Dan asked in unison.

"Yes, we do!" Johnny answered. "$50.00."

"How do you know the exact amount?" Dan asked.

"I saw an advertisement in the Marshalltown newspaper."

George blurted, "Farmer Luther Robertson, on the north edge of town wants to hire us to help him do chores."

"It's close enough, we can walk there easily," Johnny said.

"How much will he pay?" Emma asked

Johnny, speaking both as the president and treasurer of the printing company, said, "One dollar a day for the two of us! Then we can make money doing print jobs and help you and dad with the bills." His good-intentions warmed Emma's heart.

Dan cautioned, "Farm work is good, but you must not neglect your school work. Johnny implemented his plan that very Saturday and learned how hard farm life could be. They helped Mr. Robertson dig post holes, stretch wire fence, shovel hog manure, hitch up the team, chase down six run-away piglets, unhitch the team, milk the cow and help Mrs. Robertson churn butter. The next day they did it all over again, except for the pig chasing. It was hot dirty work, but they were getting paid. When George got discouraged, Johnny reminded him of how much fun they'd have running their printing press. "And we'll become famous newspaper publishers."

By fall, they made enough chore money to buy the little printing press. Daniel helped them set it up in a corner of the mud room off the kitchen. Emma observed, "All three of my boys seem excited." Dan said, "It brings back good memories from my Oregon days."

Both boys discovered that printing was as dirty as farm chores and printer's ink was harder to scrub off than pig manure.

Emma watched them through the kitchen door and said, "They aren't going to make much money on this printing venture, but it will do them good."

Dan agreed. "Smelling the printer's ink makes me think about reprinting my baptism booklet!" Emma warned, "Remember, you don't have the money to pay them. Let's see if they can drum up some business on their own."

But it wasn't business the Turneys drummed up; it was trouble. On October 21, Dan's sermon in Rhodes drifted into politics. Emma winced when he criticized the Republicans. 'Oh Dan, you put your boot between your teeth. This will not end well.' The simmering silence in the room erupted into an explosion of anger when the Turneys left. The lay leader chased them down the sidewalk, "Rev. Turney, you are no longer our preacher! We'll be looking for a new preacher who has some common sense! You'll have to move out of our parsonage!"

Emma dug her fingers into Dan's hand. The lay leader pivoted and left them to fend for themselves. Eventually, supporters in the St. Anthony Church found them a house to live in. It was small, but Johnny and George approved. There was a shed to house their printing business, *"Turney Brother's Printing, St. Anthony, Iowa."* They designed and printed off their business cards and gave them to anyone who'd take one. They got a small Christmas order and announced to the family, "We are officially printers!"

"Turney Brothers!" George declared.

Dan sat at his desk, crowded into a corner of the tiny dining room. Watching the boys helped him realize how depressed he felt. 'How often have I said- when we're knocked down by life, we have to get up again.' He picked up his pen and began writing an inquiry letter.

1895

It was a hard winter- snow, ice and influenza. Everyone suffered, but Emma was hit hardest. Dan was off on a speaking trip when Emma got so sick with the grip that she had to impose on a neighbor to take her to the doctor. He gave her a prescription for a celery compound, "Let's try this new medicine, since nothing else has worked, Mrs. Turney." She used it as directed and was amazed at how quickly her health was restored. She raved about it to Dan, when he returned. She slipped some into his morning coffee and he seemed to feel better too. Then she gave some to all three children. Dan teased her, "You need to write a testimonial to the company that made this magic potent.

She agreed and slid behind his desk and began writing, "My husband and three children were greatly benefited by the use of Paine's Celery Compound as I was after an unusually hard siege of the grip, with variations of the disease. We regard the compound as a most remarkable remedy...."

She was shocked two weeks later when she got a fat letter from Wells-Richardson and Company of Burlington, Vermont asking to publish her letter and a photograph of her entire family in a national campaign. "If your family photograph meets our needs, we will include it in our fall campaign. You will be handsomely compensated. Below is a listing of newspapers we advertise in." It included every major paper in the country- from Buffalo, New York to St. Louis, Missouri, to Chicago, Illinois, to Salinas, Kansas to Vicksburg, Mississippi to Salt Lake City, Utah, to Los Angeles, California.

"Maggie, come here, you won't believe this!" She spread the pages across the table. Johnny and George followed Maggie into the room.

Johnny picked up the list. "Mom, these are the biggest papers in the country!"

"And they want a picture of our family!" George exclaimed.

Emma cautioned, "They want to see our picture before they promise anything."

"That's too bad," Johnny said. "Who would pay good money for a picture of a country bumpkin preacher's family?"

"Wells-Richardson will if it helps sell their product.," Emma said.

When Dan got home, he immediately scheduled a family photo shoot. They mailed the picture to Vermont and waited. Just as Emma's money jar was emptied, she got a three-sentence contract from Vermont and a check. Their photo and article would be featured in the October national campaign. Emma cashed the check and replenished her emergency fund. Dan got good news the same week. He handed Emma a letter he'd just torn open. "I've been invited to preach down in Milton, Iowa in March. I have a baptism debate over in Des Moines next month. Those offerings should help. God is providing, Emma!"

"I know he is, Dan. I just worry about the children."

HERE'S A WHOLE FAMILY.

Husband, Wife and Children Made Well by Paine's Celery Compound.

The pre-eminence of Paine's celery compound over all other remedies could not e better illustrated than in the case of the Turney family of St. Anthony, Iowa.

Mrs. Turney had recovered her health by the use of Paine's celery compound.

She had suffered from a variety of ills, all due to a nervous system improperly nourished.

Their real trouble is a run-down condition of the nerves and blood, and Paine's celery compound, as in the case of Mrs. Turney and her family, will make them well again.

Rheumatism and neuralgia too grow more dangerous and more painful with cold weather.

This increased pain points to increased activity of these disorders.

There is positive danger in allowing the system to meet the perils of winter

The Evening Express (Lost Angeles, CA) 26 Oct 1895. 12

The 55 member St. Anthony church didn't like Dan being gone so much, but understood. "We can't pay more and your family needs to eat." Emma and Maggie planted their garden. Johnny and George learned they could not make a living in the printing business and needed to finish school. Dan wrote another letter to the Milton M P. church and gave them his sermon titles for March 24th and 25th.

CHAPTER TWENTY

Milton, Iowa
1895

On March 23, Dan took the first of many train rides from Marshall County to Van Buren County, Iowa. He preached at the Milton Methodist Protestant Church. The nine-year-old congregation had a big building at Main Street and the state road. Folks bragged, "We're at the junction of main and main!" Dan hit it off with them. They were regular folks who were impressed with his eloquence. Dan scheduled a six-day baptismal debate to be hosted by the Milton Methodist Protestants and the Milton Christian Church. One of his new friends said, "I hope we can argue with them without becoming enemies!"

"Dan said, "We can! Rev. Creel and I are good friends, even if we see different truths about baptism in the bible. We're not trying to make anybody angry; we just want you to think a little deeper."

They liked what he said. "How about you come back and preach the circuit on the weekend before the debate?" Dan asked about the preaching schedule. "On Sunday April 28, you'll preach here at Milton at 11am, then over at Cantril at 3pm, and Mt Zion at 7pm."

"Is Mt. Zion the country church?"

"One of them. There's also South Prairie. It's smaller."

"I'll see you next month, then!"

On the train ride home, he was thankful the church leaders would chauffer him around. Dan knew he could get lost on his way back from the outhouse. Soon, he was back at St. Anthony, checking on the kids' school work, spending precious moments with Emma and prepping for the upcoming debate with Creel. Johnny said, "Those Milton folks best put on their thinking caps!"

"Right you are, Johnny. But I have to put mine on first. Emma, there's a lot of interest down there. I may have found us another place to put down roots."

"Dan, whenever you say that, I feel like I'm about to be uprooted and transplanted!"

"Some plants grow better in new soil," he said.

"That may be true, but plants are also most vulnerable during transplanting!" He caught her warning and gave her a hug.

"I wish I could go down with you…"

"But the children need you here," he finished her sentence. "Em, it will be worth it. Creel and I expect big crowds. The local paper is giving us great coverage!"

"You always like seeing your name in print," Emma said.

"If it gets more people to come to services. Bigger crowds, bigger responses."

"And bigger collections," she teased.

"Bigger offerings wouldn't hurt," he said.

"Might even help us," Emma admitted.

Dan said, "I'm so confident, I'll get someone to plant us a garden in Milton!"

"Corn, green beans, tomatoes, squash, peas…."

"Dan stopped her, "Make me a list. You know how I can forget details."

"I do. I will make my garden wish list."

Three weeks later Dan had Emma's list tucked into his travel coat pocket next to his sermon notes. His debate plans were scattered in the pages of his study bible. His valise of books and two clean shirts sat on the empty seat beside him. He was as edgy as a mare ready to foal. Dan opened a book and tried to read his way from Marshalltown to

Ottumwa. He'd change trains before reaching Milton. He didn't get very far into his latest scholarly journal when an idea sparked in his mind. He picked up his note pad and jotted down the words before they disappeared. Nothing irritated him more than to have a great idea and then to lose it into the morning light like an untethered kite floating into the clouds. "Some of my best ideas are floating around somewhere out there," he mumbled.

A traveling salesman across the aisle thought he was striking up a conversation, but soon discovered that wasn't the case. Dan didn't waste precious reading time in frivolous conversations. Emma once suggested, "Listening to folks might help them listen to you." He knew she right, but he had debates to prepare for.

On Tuesday, April 30, the first debate began. Debates were marathon events, not sprints. A debater once joked, "The spectators keep coming back just to see which one of us will drop first." Dan enjoyed the repartee and valued the friendship he and Creel had developed in their years of sparring, jabbing and feinting in the intellectual boxing ring.

The Milton Methodist Protestant building was packed, with a line from the foyer down the steps, spilling out onto the street. Turney and Creel had never seen anything like it. The rules of the debate were read by a moderator, introductions made and the debate began. Elder Creel stepped to the pulpit. The air crackled with excitement.

An hour later, D.B. Turney took the stage. He spoke respectfully of Elder Creel, before dismantling his argument. It was a verbal war. Intellectual bullets and biblical bombs were lobbed back and forth. When the first day was done, enthusiasm flamed. Word spread and by the May 7th conclusion, the crowd outside encircled the jammed building. Curious faces pressed to the open windows to listen. Preachers from dozens of denominations traveled half-way across Iowa to be there. The six-hour-a-day, six-day event become a phenomenon. The Milton newspaper said, "It has done much toward educating the people of this community to a higher plane of religious thought and inculcated a greater respect for the views of those with whom we differ. All agree as to the ability and scholarship of the combatants and the able and thorough manner in which the questions were discussed. It was no small honor to our city to be the place chosen for so an important event."

Before the debate ended, M. P. church leaders asked D. B. Turney to become their preacher. Dan agreed and gave them Emma's garden list. A farmer looked it over and said, "That woman knows how to garden." Two families, who preferred working with their hands to listening to debates, were planting the garden before Dan took the train back to St. Anthony.

Although Turney would not officially become their preacher until early October, he returned to preach on May 13 and September 29. On October 12, he preached his first official sermon as their pastor. Son George said, "I've never seen so many people in church!" They were off to a marvelous start.

Dan had barely settled into Milton, when he trekked off to Ohio for another debate. He returned to Iowa and stopped by the post office. He was eager to open the package from Vermont, hoping for a Paine's Celery Compound bonus check. He tore open the heavy parcel and found the original family photograph they had mailed months ago. Next to the photo was a thank you letter and a carefully wrapped bottle of the medicine. Dan held the bottle to the light, 'What makes this concoction work so well?' Turning the square bottle, he saw the list of ingredients: Celery Seed, Red Cinchona Officinalis, Orange Peel, Coriander Seed, Lemon Peel.... He gulped when he read the next ingredient- Alcohol. "Alcohol is a major ingredient!" he bellowed. Emma rushed into the room. His face was red with anger. "Emma do you know what we endorsed? Paine's Celery Compound is nothing but alcohol gussied up as medicine!"

Emma couldn't look him in the eye, "I didn't read the label until after I sent the testimonial. I was afraid to tell you."

Clutching the bottle, Dan headed for the door, "I'm pouring this vile, deceitful brew into the weeds out back. Don't tell anyone what was in it. I'll be the laughing stock of town and get expelled from the Prohibition Party. The door slammed behind him. Emma walked to the window and blurted out, "I'm not sorry we took the medicine! I'm not sorry we got better!" She watched him empty the bottle, grab a garden spade and bury it behind the shed.

When he came back, she had composed herself. "Rev. Turney, we have nothing to be ashamed of! You did not knowingly betray your righteous principles! You'll see that after you cool down." She was right. Emma would often chuckle about the irony of a prohibitionist family testifying to the positive benefits of alcohol. It would be years before Dan could laugh about it. He reluctantly set aside his prohibition lectures and focused on preaching.

In early December, he traveled to Missouri for another baptism debate. Johnny joked, "Mom, did you know that if you cut off the southern tier of Iowa's counties and add them to Missouri, you raise the IQ of both states."

"That's not a kind thing to say, Johnny!"

Emma was glad Dan's share of the debate collections helped the family income, but hoped he wasn't spreading himself too thin. While debating in Missouri, Dan connected with a M.P. leader, who talked him into transferring to the Missouri Conference. On Dec 28, he officially joined the Missouri conference, but kept preaching in Iowa's Milton circuit.

1896

The four congregations on the Milton Circuit, like most M.P. churches, struggled financially. Dan talked with Emma about their plight. She said, "No wonder you're getting on so well here- they're as poor as we are."

"I wish I knew how to help them," he lamented.

Emma's eyes lit up. "You remember how the Tipton church struggled with their debt?"

"How could I forget!"

"Remember what Rev. Moulton did to help them?"

"After we left," Dan said, "he held a series of meetings. The collections paid off the debt." He jumped out of his chair, "I could do that. We could hold protracted meetings in each church. Crowds will come!"

"So, will collections!" Emma said.

Dan shared the idea with his churches. Leaders agreed. A long-time member said, "We can reach new folks and raise money for our church at the same time."

"Might even do us old-salts some good!" another added. A third piped in, "It might just work. Turney, you're getting sort of famous around here. We have our very own William Jennings Bryan." They agreed to begin extended services.

Dan started at Milton on Wednesday night, January 15, with a public lecture called "The nationalization of money." The Milton newspaper promoted it, "The lecture is given for purpose of defraying the church debt. No doubt this will be a very interesting lecture as Mr. Turney is an able man." Admission was set at $1.00. Dan told Emma, "It's a start!" They held meetings in Milton for five weeks, concluding on Sunday March 15. It was a success. One key leader thanked Dan, "We had quite a number of converts and the offerings benefitted the church." He conducted similar meetings in Mt. Zion beginning in late January. Dan got so busy, he had to ask former Milton pastor H.C. Dameron to come back to help with the preaching

Dan launched protracted meetings in South Prairie Chapel Church just as he finished at Milton and Mt. Zion. That series lasted until mid-April. Cantril was the last on the circuit to get its turn.

Maggie complained that her dad did nothing but preach. George defended his father, "Sis, he is a preacher!" Johnny was relieved he didn't have to sit through all his dad's sermons. Both he and George were intrigued by Daniel's May 17th sermon, "Infinite Infiniteness, or the Infiniteness of Small Things." At Sunday dinner, Johnny asked, "Dad, where do you come up with all your ideas?"

"In my study or reading my bible. Sometimes inspiration just comes out of the blue. I'm thinking of doing another sermon like today's, but I'll call it 'The Littleness of Great Things!'" George got it, "Sometimes little things are great and great things are little." Dan rumpled George's hair. Maggy asked, "I'm still little, can I be great?"

"Of course," Emma affirmed.

"By the way," Dan said, "I'm considering another debate with Elder J.C. Creel."

"Where?" they asked.

"LaHarpe, Illinois."

"That's where I was born!" Maggie exclaimed.

"You're right!" Dan said. "And that's where I met Elder Creel."

"Will we move back there?" Maggie asked.

"No. I'm just going there to speak." Dan didn't have the heart to tell the children that he knew their time in Milton, Iowa would end soon.

When Iowa church leaders learned that D.B. Turney had transferred to the Missouri Conference, they assumed he was planning to move, so they began searching for a new pastor to serve the Milton Circuit. Milton's lay leader said, "Rev. Turney, we appreciate your hard work in getting us out of debt. We owe you. Stay in the parsonage as long as you need to. We'll make other housing arrangements for the new preacher." They were relieved not to move. Johnny could finish his senior year in Milton.

1897

When Johnny graduated on April 30, the Turneys squeezed into a short pew at the Milton High School Commencement held in the Christian church. Dan liked the class of '97 motto- *The Marble Awaits the Sculptor*. He pointed it out to Emma, "That would make a worthy sermon title!" The processional interrupted her answer. Parents watched as their children marched toward adulthood. During the program, John E.Z. Turney sang with the choir, received academic recognition and gave an oration he'd titled, "Comical Evolution."

In early August, Dan told the family, "I'm off for Chicago this week. I hope to get a publisher interested in my book *Hesperus!*" Emma wasn't sure if he'd been inspired by the poet Longfellow or by the Greeks. John flipped through the manuscript and thought he had it figured out. George and Maggie didn't get it.

Dan's August 11 book trip to Chicago was not a total loss. Nobody liked his book, but his interview with an Indiana Methodist

Protestant leader produced a job offer to be a conference missionary in the western half of the state. There was a small stipend, but he had to find his own housing and a church to serve. He told them, "I'll have to talk with my wife Emma, but am ready for a new challenge." On the train home, he thought of how they began their marriage in Edgar County, Illinois, just across from the Indiana state line. 'What if we could find a place to live and serve there?' Emma liked the idea.

CHAPTER TWENTY-ONE

Eastern Illinois and Indiana
Oct. 1897

Old friends in Edgar County wrote them about a tiny church in Brouillett's Creek Township that had a parsonage and needed a preacher. The writer warned, "The church has struggled and hasn't had a full-time pastor for years. But they're good folks and would like you and Emma to come."

Dan called the family together, "George, you asked where we are going next. Now we know- it's Edgar County, Illinois."

Emma reminded them, "It's the county where we spent our first year of marriage."

"I'm going to be a missionary for the Indiana M.P. Church Conference," Dan said.

"But we'll live in Illinois?" John asked.

"Yes. Our house is just a stone's throw from Indiana." Dan answered.

"What about schools?" they asked.

Emma said, "Maggie, your school will be right across the road from our house."

George squirmed in his chair. "Count me out. I'm staying in Milton to finish high school."

"Where will you live?" Emma asked.

"Elmer McManis said I could stay with his folks. They live just a few blocks from school."

"You'll get to graduate from Milton High, even if the rest of us move," John said.

They absorbed the idea of moving without George. Dan broke the silence, "John, there are colleges in eastern Illinois."

John locked eyes with his father, "I'll need a job before I can afford college."

"There's a big printing company in the county seat of Paris," Dan said.

"Paris, like in France?" Maggie asked

"Take me back to *ol' Paree,*" John snarked. "What town will we live in?"

Dan mumbled, "It's not a town; just a cluster of houses, a church and a cemetery."

On October 22, the family left George behind and headed to eastern Illinois. They settled in quickly. Emma chirped, "Many hands make a light load." Dan began his work as a M.P. missionary in western Indiana. He roamed through farm country and found a scattering of tiny, struggling churches. Dan sampled home cooking in several parsonages and fished for preaching invitations, but churches often felt both too small and too poor to hold extended missions. Most of his preaching was done in the dilapidated church near Owl Creek in Edgar County, Illinois. From his study window, Dan watched the creek twist its way behind the cemetery.

Maggie said, "It feels spooky. Owls hooting and cemetery ghost's floating."

Dan did not comment. He furiously wrote letters to Indiana newspapers. Few got published. "Emma, I'm not being as well received as I was in Cairo or Milton!"

"Rev. Turney, they don't know you over in Indiana!"

He agreed. "Maybe I should spend more time in Illinois." He convinced his supervisor into 'loaning' him to the S. IL Conference.

Dan supplemented his meager church salary with speaking engagements and debates wherever he could beg an invitation.

Oldest son John adjusted to Edgar County. He found part-time farm work shucking corn. He'd harness a mule to a back-board wagon and drive into a ripe field of corn. His job was to snap the ear of corn off the stalk and throw it into the wagon. Two of his co-workers got competitive. A rapid rain of ears hammered the backboard. John was fit and showed them how fast he could fill a wagon. "Turney," one of them yelled, "you're making the rest of us look bad!"

"Not hard to do!" John replied as he snapped two ears at once and flipped them into the wagon. He finished his load before noon, which was unheard of. Someone accused him of filling the bottom of the load with rocks. Another said, "You worked last night with help from the spooks at Owl Creek Cemetery."

"Funny folks live there and you should hear them sing on Sundays," John badgered back, "I dare you to come to church!"

Rising to the bait, a wagon load showed up at Owl Creek Church on Sunday morning. They stomped in, demanding attention and asking questions. It stirred up regular church folk, who were not used to riff-raff. Emma, younger and gutsier than most church goers, confronted the ruffians, "Come on in and sit. We have some right good treats after the sermon.

"We hear you serve D.B. Turney dumb cakes."

Emma bristled, "That's not a nice thing to say in church."

"Well, we heard this church's preacher is named Daniel Bonehead Turney. Is that true?"

An old farmer warned, "Boys, careful with your words!"

The ringleader replied, "Old man, there's several of us here this morning. It'd be a shame for all these fancy pew benches to get broken up." He held up a hymn book. "And for your pretty song books to get all tore up!"

John, tried to stand up tall. "My Pappy will be here shortly. No one can stop him from preaching. You wreck this building and he can preach in the woods on a stump."

"I s'pose he could walk across the creek and preach to the ghosts in the cemetery!"

Gaining confidence, John replied, "I reckon he could preach to the dead, but think he might prefer to preach to you half-dead guys." The ruffians moved toward him, just as D.B. Turney burst through the doorway, a big bible in his left hand. "Gentlemen, we've got plenty of seats left. If you can stomach some truth!"

One-by-one, they sat down in seats that were usually empty. One mumbled, "My clothes ain't good enough for no fancy church."

Emma said, "Don't worry. The Lord doesn't judge us by what we wear, but by what we do."

The piano player played a calming old gospel tune, followed by an up-tempo congregational favorite. Regulars and newcomers were soon caught up in the singing. Dan stepped to the pulpit and preached. The *corn boys,* as John called them, were jolted by a hail storm of some of the biggest words in the English language. When the preacher finally took a breath, one boy said, "I never heard no one talk like this before!" The sermon that morning was about how God seeks to save lost sinners.

The ringleader got the message and shook his fist, "You're talking about me and my boys, preacher man! You making fun of us?"

"No sir." Dan said. "We all sin and fall short of the glory of God, whether we're preachers, farm workers, blacksmiths or boat men. We all need the Lord. Owl Creek M.P. is here to tell everyone that good news. I invite you to come to the Lord's table."

The church steward lifted the white tablecloth and revealed the loaf of bread and the chalice of grape juice. Turney intoned, "The Lord's table is open to all who would put their trust in Jesus Christ." The corn boys were surprised to be included and church folks were surprised when they clomped forward for a piece of bread and a sip of juice from the old golden cup. D.B. Turney had made it clear that ALL who wanted more of Jesus were welcome. The hungry working men went forward.

One admitted, "Rev. Turney, "This could be the best day of the week." Dan agreed and gave them the short version of his sabbath sermon. They stayed around for coffee and cookies. The ringleader apologized to John, "Sorry. We didn't mean no harm to your father. We got to go and unload our corn. You want to help us?" John followed them to the wagons.

He told his parents, "I'm going to start my ride down to Effingham. I cribbed my corn last night and I packed a sandwich."

"You have water?" Emma asked.

"Our biggest jug. Also, remember I start work part-time at Colson's printing company next week." He gave Maggie a hug and mounted his horse and followed the corn boys.

1898-1899

John was a part-time student at Austin College, Maggie started high school. George finished high school in Milton, Iowa and moved to Illinois to became a teacher at Adam's grade school, across the road from the Turney's house.

"Mom," George fretted, "there is no clock in my room and I can't afford to buy a watch. How can I know when school starts or ends?"

"I have an idea. You can see our house from your school house window. What if I put out a dish towel on the window ledge, to signal when it's time for the opening bell, recess, lunch and dismissal?"

"Thanks mom. As long as it's not dad who hangs out the signal. He's just gone too much for me to depend on."

Emma nodded, "And even when he's home, reading in his study, he'd just as well be in Paris."

"Illinois or France?" George asked.

"Either. You know how his mind wanders."

Later that night, Dan complimented Emma on her idea. "George will be a good teacher, with your help." Towel duty never occurred to the preacher.

"Dan, he's saving for college. He and John both plan to go full-time to Austin College next year. Our children are almost grown!" He saw the tears welling up in her eyes and reached over and gave her a shoulder squeeze.

CHAPTER TWENTY-TWO

Effingham, Illinois
Fall 1900

That fall, the Turneys moved to Effingham, Illinois. Printer John and teacher George became full-time students at Austin College. Maggie attended high school. Dan preached in a small church and Emma coordinated their busy lives. They rented an old house near the Austin campus. Dan transferred back to S. IL Conference and resumed his travel pattern of speeches and debates.

Maggie's best conversations with her father happened during walks to the train station. She would sit with him on a polished wooden bench and wait for the train. She knew he was an unusual man. Her classmates would call him 'odd'. She considered him 'special'. Who else would talk with his teenage daughter about John Milton, mathematics, Greek diction and scientific theories? She soaked in his words until a distant train whistle intruded. Dan stood, hefted his big carpet bag over his left shoulder and picked up the small one with his right hand. Maggie had watched him fill the big bag with a dozen books, his writing pad and a battered bible. The lighter bag had only a pair of clean socks, an extra shirt and the lunch Emma had packed. He avoided a public hug and said, "Off I go to Cairo!" His rhyme put a smile on both their faces.

Maggie watched him stride toward the platform. He wore the same old black coat he'd worn when she was a toddler. His old silk hat had been soaked by the rain of a hundred storms. Her mother once said, "Dan, you've worn the nap right off your hat." He replied, "My dear, we live hand-to-mouth, I can't afford a new one."

Turney stepped onto the train and waved one more time. Maggie sat on the bench until the caboose disappeared.

D.B. Turney loved traveling. His little church had services only twice a month, so he was free to trek far and wide. He connected with M.P. preachers and churches all over southern Illinois. They were a small, beleaguered bunch. Turney's scholarly lectures were a diversion in their bleak intellectual landscapes. Emma complained, "Sometimes you seem more married to your train trips than you are to me. We write more than we talk." On May 30, 1902, she sent him a postcard reminding him to be back in Effingham for the boy's June 8-12 commencement,

"...I look for you the first of the week...Report has it that Mr. and Mrs. Conover will be in Effingham for John and George's commencement...I am not reading so much for a while, letting my eyes rest and get used to the glasses I bought from a vendor.

I don't like for you to be away so long when you go so often anyway. So, hurry home, will you? I didn't get used to your absences in 27-years of time, I never will, will I? -Much love, yours Emma V.O. Turney"

The post card chased D.B. Turney across southern Illinois, but didn't catch him. It returned to Effingham before he did. Emma crumpled the card and pounded the table in a rare fit of anger. "Maggie, your father is going to miss Austin's Class Day Exercise tonight!"

George, who was trying on his college graduation gown for the third time, rushed to his mother and hugged her trembling shoulders.

143

"Mom, it will be OK. There's still another train coming from the south."

John dashed into the room, "George, we've got to get moving. We can't be late or our rehearsal. Mom, we'll see you and Maggie at the Opera House."

"Your father isn't here yet!"

"Well, we'll have to go ahead without him, then!" John barked.

An hour south, D.B. Turney paced on the Marion train station platform, weighed down by his bags and poor planning. He glanced at his pocket watch for the umpteenth time. The Illinois Central train to Effingham was ten minutes late. "Come on! Come on! I can't let them down. It was a muddle-headed mistake taking that extra jaunt down to Cairo to see my old friend." He fanned his sweating face with his old hat. When he heard the train whistle, he danced a jig, jogged along beside the slowing train, climbed aboard and grabbed the closest seat to the door. Traveling north, he gained back five of his lost minutes. Would it be enough? Dan knew he was in the dog house and rushed from the station to their house, puffing to catch his breath. He shrugged off his heavy coat and it trailed behind him as he reached his yard. Climbing the front porch steps, he saw a note fastened to the door. Dan dropped his bags and opened the note addressed to "Rev. D. Turney." The message stabbed him in the heart.

Meanwhile, Emma and Maggie had hitched a ride to Effingham's Austin Opera House. "Mom, it's so big!" Maggie exclaimed.

"Not sure it's big enough for today's crowd," Emma said as they pushed their way through the throng. Inside, Austin College banners and posters festooned every column and wall. "Let's find seats on an aisle. We can save a place for your father."

Maggie smirked, "I wasn't sure you'd let him sit with us!" Emma gritted her teeth to choke back what she wanted to say. They found center aisle seats in the middle of the cavernous room. Both began reading their programs. Maggie found when John and George would be speaking. "I hope they like John's poem," she whispered. "I thought it was great!"

"He read it to you?"

"Last night." Maggie said.

"John wouldn't let me see it." Emma lamented. "Wanted me to hear it tonight from the stage."

Back at the house, Dan leaned against the front door and read the poetic note from Emma,

"Crowds may think thee great,
But not your family when you're late!
To forget us is a deed too vile to discuss,
We have gone on without thee.
I am a deeply disappointed, me;
My sons have made me glad.
My husband has made me sad!"

He pushed the door open, wiping away tears of guilt. He piled his bags on a chair, rushed to the sink, washed away the travel dust before bolting back onto the street. "Hurry, Hurry, Dan," he chided himself.

A neighbor slowed his buggy and asked the winded preacher, "Rev. Turney, you need a ride the Opera House?"

"Desperately," he grunted as he climbed into the passenger seat. "You are an answer to an unuttered prayer.

"Never heard of that kind of prayer, preacher."

"Neither has the Lord," Dan said. "Sometimes even unasked prayers are answered." God's rescuing chariot wasn't driven by an angel, but by Bill Baxter.

Baxter announced, "I'll drop you at the front door."

Dan thanked him, jumped out to join the crush of latecomers pushing through the doorway. He walked in on an instrumental version of "Toujours Belle". The crowd stood properly, but D.B. Turney muscled his way through, ignoring social protocol, his eyes darting from side to side. Reaching the front of the crowd, he spotted George among the students solemnly marching down the left aisle. Searching the right column, he saw John, eyes fixed on the student ahead of him. "Now to find Emma and Maggie," he muttered loudly enough to earn a nasty look. "There they are, halfway down the center aisle!" Daniel marched down the aisle, in lockstep with the robed students moving up the side aisles toward the stage. He ignored the indignant stares and squeezed in beside Emma, just as John and George took their seats on the platform. Dan's hand touched Emma and he whispered, "I'm sorry." She kept her eyes properly ahead, but gave his hand a light squeeze.

Dan leaned back into his seat. He knew Emma would eventually forgive him. This moment belonged to the boys. Austin College had an eleven-year Class Day Program tradition. Every graduate delivered a tribute, oration, prophecy or poem. Dan, Emma and Maggie waited for George J.'s turn. George followed Olive Morton to the podium, keeping his bearing and delivering a tribute to oratory. Dan smiled. He had helped George craft his speech. Maggie poked him, "George has his daddy's public poise." Seven presentations later, John E.Z. delivered the class poem with flair and confidence. He had written it without his father's help. All the Turneys loved poetry. The lengthy program concluded with the class of 1902 singing their class song. Dan knew his boys didn't get their musical ability from him. He could hear Emma and Maggie singing along with the graduates.

On Thursday, Dan tried to make amends for his Tuesday tardiness by attending chapel services. John had let it slip that George would have a big role in the service. Retiring professor T.F. Heckert was being recognized by students, faculty and the entire community. He was given a gold watch and an elegant set of Rudyard Kipling's novels. Heckert was juggling his gifts as George J. Turney stepped to the podium and led a round of applause for the professor. "It is my privilege to represent the senior class and all the classes before us who have benefitted from Professor Heckert's skills. His is one of the most popular and successful teachers ever connected with the college. His resignation has caused a unanimous feeling of deep regret among the students and faculty. The department he has built, the friendships his kind heart has formed and the manly model of true character he has set before the school and community are and ever will be his eternal monuments." George strode over to Heckert, gave him a bear hug,

"We thank you as we step forward from Austin into the world. We're better men and women having known you!"

Emma whispered to Dan, "George sure could have used a watch like that, when he started teaching,"

"Wish we could buy him one," Dan said as he hurried down the aisle to catch George, before he exited the chapel. He clapped George on the back, "Great job with the speech! I hope when I retire that someone will say, "D. B. Turney, built eternal monuments.""

George replied, "Dad, you major in the eternal, don't you?"

That night, Dan, Emma and Maggie were back in the Austin Opera House, waiting for John and George to walk on stage again. The commencement had all the usual bells and whistles. The class of 1902 was recognized as the largest in Austin College's history. The Turneys waited patiently as degrees were conferred alphabetically; at last they got to "St.Clair, Seltz and Spiker." Dan was on the edge of his seat, when Professor Heckert broke protocol and read two names at once, "John E.Z. Turney and his brother George J. Turney." They marched together in double-time across the stage to receive their Bachelor of Arts degrees. When Professor Heckert gave George his diploma, he declared, "Thanks for your magnificent speech earlier!" Dan jumped to his feet and applauded. Maggie and her mother blushed. John exited the stage, saw his father standing, and waved. George waved too. Dan waved back. Emma covered her face.

That day changed their lives forever. John left Effingham to become principal at Bement, Illinois High School. George became a teacher at Humboldt School in Coles County, Illinois, north of Mattoon. Maggie entered the elementary teachers' program at Austin College. Dan hit the road after being elected President of the S. IL Methodist Protestant Church that fall. Emma felt left behind; everyone's worlds were expanding, hers was shrinking. So, she focused on practical skills like raising asparagus, sweet corn, beans and beets. On the rare days when Dan was home, his attention was consumed in a maze of intellectual pursuits. He chased down obscure meanings of Greek, Hebrew or Persian words. One writer accused him of knowing 26 languages. In a humble moment, he admitted to Emma, "It's probably only 18." He got into a word debate with a Professor Macy, half-way across the country on proof-texting a single Greek word.

Dan looked over the top of his glasses and gave her his best professorial pose, "Words matter, my dear, especially the small ones."

"Don't look down your nose at me, even if you're smartified-up with your prestigious D.D. and L.L. D. honorary degrees. I've read many books and I have honorary degrees in gardening, cookery, laundering and money-stretching."

Her words punched through. "Em, I'm sorry to be such a nitwit. I know I get fixated on my ideas and forget the practical stuff you care for every day."

She smiled. "I've never met anyone who could chase as many ideas at once as you can. I guess that's what drew me to you. What's the Greek word for that?"

Daniel looked over his glasses again, "Actually, there are four Greek words for love- agape, eros...."

"Dr. Turney, stick to English."

"Emma, I love you."

"That's the language I want you to speak and those are words a wife loves hearing!" She walked over to him, took of his glasses and kissed him. "Dan, let's not get lost in a feud over words and miss out on each other."

"Em, you have such a great heart!"

She replied, "You too, but sometimes you hide it under your big brain. Put away that old book and come to bed."

The next morning, he caught a train to St. Louis to begin visiting his churches. But his mind stayed on Emma, his sweet Em of Effingham. He rode contentedly without opening a book, checking his schedule or jotting a sermon note. Leaving St. Louis, Dan zig-zagged east and south across southern Illinois. As Conference President, his job was to encourage preachers and churches and help them discern God's leading. He did his best, but sometimes felt like a hippopotamus trying to fly to the top of a pine tree. Some preachers, who found out about his new honorary degrees, tried to butter him up by calling him 'Dr. Turney'. Others, who hated church bureaucracy, ignored his titles. Most folks were glad for a listening ear, a thoughtful sermon and some good ideas. As his village-hopping tour ended, Daniel sat down to write his report for The Methodist Recorder. He began with a question,

"Does anybody think Union Circuit is on the prairie? If so, he (or she) misses the mark. That portion of Illinois is a surprise to many… It has hills, rocks, sand-tone boulders, caves, gullies and trees of various sorts. Bro. B.S. Billings, our pastor there, is greatly beloved among the people. Wherever I went, persons in the church, and not in it, had words of commendation for him. I preached at Farmers Bluff, using I John 5:1 as my text. Unfortunately, the morning service on October 4 was rained entirely out. Brother Billings and I vainly attempted to reach Cedar Grove that evening, but a washed-out dirt culvert forced us back on Bro. Russell's ready hospitality. It gave us a chance to see the massive sandstone fortification, with the cave and the spring and other points worth noting. Of course, we visited Mt. Joy and Mt. Olive, as well as Liberty. I preached using texts from Romans 1:16, I John 5:4 and Psalm 97:1.

At Marion, Brother W.S. Beers came for me in his buggy and gave me a delightful ride to his home on Harrisburg Circuit, near Dillingham chapel. While there, I met old-time friends Hon. W.D. Dewoody and Rev. M.S. Strike. I believe they would have kept me with them for a month if they could. Later, I met William V. Rush and his wife who had known me thirty years ago on Metropolis Circuit. Back then I was like the preacher who said he intended 'to ride the circuit even if he had to walk.'"

Dan described a few more encounters in Southeast Illinois and concluded with, "It is delightful to know that God's people in the Methodist Protestant Church are alive to the touch of power. Let us pray much, and trust continually in God's grace, and the work of our Zion shall prosper in the Lord…."

The Turney family gathered around their 1903 Thanksgiving dinner table. John and George swapped stories about teaching and teachers. Maggie enjoyed the good stories and winced at the bad ones. Emma soaked it all in as she darted between the cookstove and the festive table. She served home-grown sweet potatoes, green beans and tomatoes. The turkey was a gift from Daniel's Crooked Creek church. John brought a fruitcake and teased George about bringing nothing. Emma intervened, "George, you can count this pumpkin pie as your contribution. You helped me peel it."

John said, "Speaking of sweets. I have met someone special." Emma and Maggie badgered him to say more. "Her name is Bertha," is all he would say. On June 4, 1904, J. E. Z. Turney wed Bertha Helen Leise at Philo in Champaign, IL. The couple moved to Potomac, IL, where he'd been named Superintendent of Schools. George was jealous. John had a wife and was already a superintendent, just two years after finishing college.

As soon as the wedding was over, Dan packed for his trip to the National Prohibition Convention in Indianapolis, Indiana. He joined a small delegation from Effingham. Ada Kepley, the first woman lawyer in the country, had put Effingham on the prohibitionist map. Her personal crusade was establishing Band of Hope, a youth-oriented temperance group. One of Kepley's longtime fans asked, "Dr. Turney, were you in Effingham when Ada was terrorized for the cause?"

"When was that?" he asked.

"1897!"

"No. We got here in the fall of 1900. What happened?"

The historian said, "An angry saloon-keeper's son broke into Kepley's home and tried to shoot her. He missed, but wounded one of her dogs. There's a price to be paid for the stands we take."

"Right you are," Dan said. "I've never been shot at, but I've been tomatoed, egged and stoned by the saloon crowd."

Impressed, the Effingham native asked, "Were you one of our party's state presidential electors?"

"Yes, I was!" D.B. Turney replied curtly. He didn't want to talk about the contentious May 27 convention in Springfield. He hoped the Indianapolis meeting would be less quarrelsome. Prohibitionists and suffragists were often accused of being agitators. It was sometimes true.

At the National Convention, Dan supported General Nelson A. Miles and spoke on his behalf. Then Miles sent a telegram, withdrawing from consideration. Eating a bit of crow, Dan threw his support behind Dr. Silas C. Swallow, the eventual nominee.

D.B. Turney could tolerate political infighting but could not stand politicians who abandoned their principles. When General Miles changed parties and abandoned the prohibitionists, Dan was incensed. He wrote a stinging op ed in the *Chicago Tribune* on July 30 rebuking Nelson, "I had hoped to see you in the White House. I believed in your patriotism, your loyalty and your magnificent manhood, but my ideal has been disappointed. I looked for you to rise superior to mere selfish ambition and show yourself the grand patriot I had pictured you to be, and I sorrowfully record my disappointment."

Dan stewed in the juices of regret. "Emma, I was a fool to go out on a limb for Nelson. I want to be a man of my word."

"Doesn't do you much good to tramp over the same ground again and again!"

He admitted, "Just makes me go in circles."

"Maybe it's time to let it go, or to begin planning your own run in 1908." She said. A new seed was planted in his fertile mind.

1905

During spring school break in 1905, John and his wife Bertha come down from Wisconsin to visit. Emma saw the glow in her face. Bertha announced, "We're going to have a baby this summer!"

Emma hugged her, "We're so happy for you and I'm happy for myself. I get to be a grandma!"

In July, John sent them a telegram, "Today, 19 July 1905 Leise Turney was born in Darius, Wisc." George, who had been touring with a tent revival group, found out about his new nephew when the musicians traveled through Effingham on their way to Arcola. George was enjoying the Union Revival Group, but had to get back to Williamsville to meet with teachers before classes started.

Maggie was enamored with George's new job, "You'll make such a good principal. And Springfield is so much closer than Wisconsin."

"I can get home more easily, but won't have a baby to bring along when I visit."

Emma quipped, "Find a wife first! We'll let John bring the baby at Thanksgiving."

In September, 1905, Daniel again presided at the annual meeting of the South Illinois M. P. Conference. He worked a grandchild reference into his ordination sermon about new beginnings. At the end of the conference, Dan was relieved of his duties as conference president. He would preach in Woodbury, north of Effingham, and again be conference polemic. He lost himself in researching obscure biblical doctrines and developing arguments against false teachings. Dan also got swept up in a tide of critics systematically attacking Mormons. A Salem, Illinois newspaper reported that his anti-Mormon lectures were "skinning them unmercifully...."

Emma didn't approve of his critical spirit and reminded him, "We are to humble ourselves, not humiliate others." On Thanksgiving Day, she paraded around with little Leise in her arms and whispered to Dan, "We are to become like little children." He couldn't debate that truth away.

Later that week, the polemic got pulled back into one of his favorite debate topics- infant baptism. A Franklin, Indiana preacher named U.C. McKinsey challenged anyone to come and debate him about baptism. "Prove that sprinkling constitutes baptism and I will give you my $12,000 farm."

Like a hungry fish, Dan hit the bait. "I can make mincemeat out of that country bumkin!" He used money they didn't have to buy a train ticket to central Indiana. The debate was a publicity hoax and never happened. Daniel wasted time and money and all he got was a mocking newspaper article and Emma's irritation. She had warned him it was a fool's errand.

1906

Dan and Emma's world stopped spinning in 1906. Their precious grandson Leise died. Emma felt something die in her heart. Nightmares dragged her back to the graves of the two babies she'd buried in Ohio. Son John, found escape from the tragedy by writing poetry. Chicago's *Interocean* newspaper named him "a valued contributor." George withdrew from children, leaving his teaching post to become a postal clerk in Decatur. Maggie couldn't process it. Dan was in Ohio debating a Texas preacher when he learned of his grandson's death. He kept preaching and writing. "I lost my grandson, but I won't lose my causes!"

That winter, Dan waded back into politics. He worked his network of old prohibition friends and convinced a few M.P. preachers to back him. Emma accused him of sending promo pieces to every newspaper in the country. "If I'm going to run for president, I will need the whole country," he said. He got some traction. On April 11, the *Tennessean* in Nashville published a piece called, 'Dauntless Dan'. Quoting another paper, "D.B. Turney for President- a peddler, printer, preacher, poet, pedagogue, philanthropist, polemic and patriot, who loves people and is loved by all who know him unless they hate what is right." It was not a full endorsement, but concluded, "We may yet be found tooting a horn in Turney's procession."

On May 3, he was endorsed by the Ministerial Association of the Methodist Protestant Church in Mt. Vernon. Illinois. *The Greensboro Daily News* reported on July 18 that Prohibitionist Carrie Nation had endorsed Daniel Braxton Turney for president, "When I say that we want a poor man's president, I mean we want a poor man for president…no rich man ought to be nominated…If any can produce the reason why Mr. Daniel Braxton Turney of Effingham, Illinois is not the man for the people's president, let him speak up now."

Emma laughed when she read it. 'Dan, how does Carrie Nation know you so well? You could be the poorest president in American history."

Dan's speech to the Methodists criticizing President Roosevelt for failing to set a good example for youth by "carrying a cigarette in his mouth and a six-shooter in his pocket" grabbed national attention. Some papers added Turney's comparing the president to an Old Testament figure, "Just as Samson did not know his strength had departed him, so our president seems ignorant of having lost his popularity, but it has gone forever."

Emma kept a scrapbook of clippings and quotes. "Dan, here's one from the *Decatur Herald*. It calls you 'MAN MENTIONED FOR PRESIDENCY', then quotes you as saying, "The local option is too local and too optional. A national disease needs a national remedy."

"We have some support in Decatur, maybe we should move there," he said, half-joking.

Emma smiled, "That is a wonderful idea. George lives there and you could launch your candidacy as the poor, prohibition, preaching president." Dan didn't like being out-worded, but he liked the possibility. They wrote to George and asked him to look for a house. George responded with a letter and sketches of three houses.

Dan told Emma, "You pick the Decatur house, I'm still trying to get into the White House. He left her in Effingham and took a political trip down to western Tennessee. He had already been endorsed by the state prohibitionist party conventions in Kentucky and Georgia. "Maybe, I can add Tennessee to my list of southern states." He made some connections in Memphis and adjoining counties, but encountered resistance. One critic challenged, "Turney, you're just a pampered, bookish preacher. You ain't no real man! A real man loves the outdoors, fishes and hunts."

Dan bristled, "I can handle a gun!"

"Prove it!" he said, poking Dan's vest. "We've got a big rifle shooting contest over in Saulsbury tomorrow. Prove you can shoot. The best pros will be there from all over the country. Big prizes."

The candidate felt cornered, "I'm not a professional. I don't shoot for a living, but I used to hunt to feed my family."

"OK, then reverend, you can shoot in the amateur class."

Dan surprised his critics, the crowd and himself by winning. His hand and eye coordination were still good. He was disappointed that cash prizes were awarded only to the professionals. He left Tennessee with an adrenaline shot to his ego and a few new political supporters. His former critic said, "I'll vote for you, just don't point your rifle my way."

CHAPTER TWENTY-THREE

Decatur, Illinois
1907

At home in Illinois, D. B. Turney's strength in the national prohibition party was sputtering. Just as they moved from Effingham to Decatur, both Dan and Emma became ill with the grip. Drained of physical strength, he canceled his engagements and was glad Maggie was there to care for them. It was a hard winter. Maggie knew her parents were recovering when Emma shook her coin jar in front of Dan, "It's almost empty!"

He wrote a pleading letter to *The Decatur Review*, "We are in pressing need of money and would welcome opportunities to preach, lecture, evangelize and hold meetings." A few days later, he was invited to Cuba, Illinois to preach a series of doctrinal sermons. Feeling better, he told Emma, "I'm not giving up on campaigning. Maybe I just need to change political directions."

"What do you mean?" she asked.

He said, "There are other prohibition- oriented political parties out there that might endorse me." He remembered an old saying of his father's, "Sometimes it's better to be a big fish in a small pond than to be a small fish in a big pond." That week, he met with a group from the United Christian party, a tiny political party based in Rock Island, IL.

One woman said, "Rev. Turney, our party principles are based on Christianity, the Ten commandments and the Golden Rule. Women's suffrage and prohibition are central issues for us." Their enthusiasm was contagious and carried D.B. Turney all the way to the United Christian party nomination convention in Rock Island, Illinois on May 1.

Dan got word that they had nominated him as their presidential candidate, with L.S. Coffin of Fort Dodge, Iowa for vice president. "Our first choice was William Jennings Bryan. He turned us down saying, 'While I believe in the application of Christian principles to public questions, I am not put under religious tests, and would not accept a nomination from any party which required religious tests.'"

Dan reassured them, "I have no problem being tested by the bible's commandments or the Golden Rule. I will gladly run on your platform."

Emma hugged him, "You've got your chance to run for president!" He laughed. "I'm already president of the S. Illinois M.P. church. We'll find out if I can be president of anything bigger." Dan still spent most of his time preaching, conducting meetings and encouraging struggling preachers and churches. Some newspapers printed his letters challenging candidates like William Jennings Bryan and Eugene Debs. D. B. Turney was endorsed by the Equal Rights Republican, American and anti-Mormon parties. He declined to be the candidate for the national Prohibition party when they refused to allow Coffin to be his running mate. Dan banned corporate campaign money and said he'd accept only half the president's salary if elected

In his stump speech, he often said, "The problems which confront our nation and the world can be solved by the political and personal application of the Ten Commandments, the Golden Rule and the wise and paternal principles of the God-honoring platform of the United Christians. All the hidden strings that bring prosperity are in the hands of God. Surely God will bless and honor the party which honors His blessed name... Relying upon the grace of God in Christ, we hope to speedily secure majority rule, direct legislation and right government...and the displacement of the rule of gold and the enthronement of the Golden Rule."

Locals enjoyed Dan's answer to J. O'Conner's question, "Hon. D.B. Turney: Which would we have, prosperity or prohibition, if United Christians win? Do not beat around the bush. Please answer in a word."

"Both," Turney answered.

On June 16, he officially launched his campaign down in Mt Vernon, IL. It didn't amount to much. Only a few old church friends, a handful of disenfranchised prohibitionists and two Anti-Mormonists showed up. It was not a newsworthy day.

Decatur newspapers were enamored with the idea of one of their own being elected president. Daniel gladly told them how he was related to both Henry Clay and James K. Polk. He was good at passing along tidbits the press could use. He enjoyed giving campaign speeches, but was oblivious to the world of filing deadlines, forms and procedures. Politician D.B. Turney resembled preacher D.B. Turney. When he boarded the train for Springfield, Missouri, the candidate wore the same beat-up hat, suit and vest that he wore for religious debates. He still carried two carpet bags, one heavy with books, the other with a change of clothes and two stump speeches. His political speeches were usually just favorite sermons, reworked.

On July 28th he spoke to a respectable crowd in Springfield, then crisscrossed Missouri on his way to Tennessee. From Memphis he went to Mississippi. On September 5 he attended the Mississippi state convention of the United Christian Party in Booneville. It was an organizational mess. Dan delivered a well-received address, but there were not enough people in attendance to select electors from throughout the state. Dan suggested they select preachers in each district and nominate them. That's what they did, without asking for their consent. It stirred up a row. Two Mississippi preachers protested to the Secretary of State, "We don't know anything about this political party and we are life-long democrats!"

The despondent candidate terminated his fruitless march through the south and retreated back to Decatur. Even the local paper poked fun at his unsuccessful campaign. When he got home, Emma handed him the *Decatur Herald's* Sept. 6 article entitled 'Turney's March Through the South.' He read it and didn't know whether to laugh or cry. "Emma, how did they know I was in Shucks, Missouri."

Emma tried not to laugh, "Who could forget that name! My favorite story was the description of you riding into Palmetto, Mississippi and speaking under a hastily erected triumphal arch. Did it really have a shield decorated with a rabbit, a rattlesnake and a bulldog?"

He guffawed, "You had to see it to believe it! I have no idea who thought that up! I need to get some rest. A month on the road is too long. Tell George and Maggie, I'll see them in the morning. After I get caught up, I'll start campaigning again."

The next day he read his mail, met with supporters, reworked another old sermon into a speech and headed out on the campaign trail. The weeks flew by. He told Emma, "I got back from Mississippi, blinked and now it's November."

"And tomorrow is election day," she reminded him, as she gave him his morning coffee.

"Someday, Emma, you will be able to go with me and cast your ballot."

"That promise would win my vote, if I had one," she said.

News reporters hounded them all day. One had done his research and discovered that D.B. Turney was called, 'a roving preacher.'

Dan shook his head, "The term we Methodists use is 'itinerant'. We are movable preachers. We go where the Lord leads."

"Dr. Turney, What's your most memorable experience as a preacher?"

He thought for a moment. "I remember when God revealed his generosity to me through his people. It was December 23, 1885 in Bureau County. I was invited to attend a lecture at Union Chapel that evening. It was a surprise party. God had inspired a group of my generous friends to collect a profusion of good things for my use. C.F. Miller led me over to a corner of the chapel and there was a huge pile of gifts- a turkey, a piece of beef., a roll of butter, a glass jar of extracted honey, three earthenware jars of lard, with quantities of sausage, potatoes, pork (enough to last the winter) beans, sugar, tea, coffee, apples, salt, soap, cabbages, onions, a few sweet potatoes and a sack of flour. Our hearts were grateful to God for every grand surprise his providence sends us!"

"That was a memorable day!" the reporter exclaimed. He turned to George, who was standing nearby. "Young man, do you expect your father to win in tomorrow's election?"

George shrugged, "Oh, no, I don't expect him to be the next president of this country. But he might slide in through some possible slip-up...at our house, we never expect to do the honors in Washington unless such an accident should occur. Dad's ambitious, I know, and he might land somewhere someday."

On election day, George and Dan went to their polling place and cast their ballots. That night, Dan went to bed at 9:30, at peace with the likely outcome. George was excited and went downtown to see what had happened. It was no surprise. D.B. Turney was walloped in Illinois. Taft got 630,020 votes, Bryan 450,702 and Turney 384.

A reporter for the *Decatur Herald* came to the house the next day and asked for a statement. Dan said, "My earnest thanks to all who supported the United Christian ticket... The election came out as I thought it would. I am not at all disappointed. I think we will have more votes in 1912. There is always the possibility of winning!"

Privately, Dan was disappointed to have lost so badly. He couldn't understand how the party missed getting on the ballot of all states except Illinois, Utah and Michigan. Turney felt the party leaders had let him down. That feeling stewed, then erupted into anger. Dan threatened to leave the party and form a new American party. "Christian people vote as they pray, with their eyes shut." In an interview about the fall election, he said, "Christians did not take advantage of the opportunities afforded them in the last election and I was defeated. The man W.R. Benkert, national chairman of the United Christians, is no worker. He made no effort to get my name on the ballot... It was only by my own private work and that of my friends that we got on three state ballots." Dan's critique concluded, "The party managers...were blockheads!"

Emma winced when she read it. Son John, up in Wisconsin, read it and fired off a letter to his father. "Dad, you need to cool down. Attacking party leaders makes you look like a sore loser."

Dan apologized, "Sorry, John. I was just letting off steam. I was just plain embarrassed to not even got on the ballot in 45 states."

In late December 1908, Decatur's *Daily Review* ran a light-hearted year-end review suggesting Decatur residents apply for government jobs "when D.B. Turney is elected president in the next election." Dan responded, "I am not inclined to count my chickens before the eggs are laid. Americans, patriots, Christians anxious to promote human welfare and the glory of God in Christ through the Holy Spirit are capable of choosing their new candidate."

CHAPTER TWENTY-FOUR

Keens, Illinois
March 8-10, 1909

Dan took a deep breath and stepped up to the small podium to launch his three-day debate with Christian church pastor Marion Boles. "Moderator, ladies and gentlemen, welcome to Keens, Illinois and our three-day debate. I will read the proposition: 'The Holy Spirit operates in direct or immediate impact on the heart of the penitent sinner in regeneration, in addition to the written or spoken word of the Lord.'

Brother Boles and I are friends... we bear each other no ill will. We both wish the truth to triumph. We admit that the Holy Spirit operates through the written word ...but scripture, history, reason and experience all teach that God is not controlled by instrumentality, that there comes a time in every case of real regeneration in which God does act directly....

(There is) an assurance that is communicated only by the direct and immediate touch of God himself to the soul...God does it. He is our only Savior. We cannot get salvation until we get it in God's way." Turney sat down.

Marion Boles stood. "This question is fraught with great consequences. Dr. Turney and I are good friends...We are here for no other purpose than to find out what the Good Book says. (We have) no questions between us as to who does the work. The only question is **how** does God do it?"

In 2 Cor. 3:3 Paul said Christians are to be letters from Christ. I have a letter here." He waved an envelope. "This is my brother's letter. Who wrote it? The Holy Spirit wrote that letter; direct down from heaven by direct personal contact? No. My brother wrote this letter using pen, ink and paper. Does Dr. Turney conceive of a letter being written without pen and paper?"

After lunch, Dan asked the crowd, "Did you notice how Brother Boles fell down before my argument that pardon is an act of divine commission, incapable of being known to us except as God reveals it to us by immediate impact of the Holy Spirit?...

At the moment the act of pardoning of sin takes place, this act is known only to God. Regeneration is an act only God can perform....it is not a thing that one man can do for another... God calls in no outside assistance." He gave the stage back to his opponent.

Boles smiled. "Dr. Turney quotes some pretty smart men, but the Bible will do for me!" He spent the rest of the afternoon quoting bible verse after bible verse.

Dan took his turn and reminded the audience that Boles had failed to address the six arguments from his first speech. "Why will he not answer? My brother ridicules the idea that children could be saved by the Holy Ghost, forgetting that John the Baptist was filled with the Holy Ghost in his mother's womb."

Boles, began his turn by asking, "If God regenerates infants before they die, why not regenerate every infant? Why do babies die? Most of them get sick. Let me help Dr. Turney out on that. When Adam and Eve were in the garden of Eden, they sinned...they became subject to death. That's why babies do not live forever." Boles walked over to Turney and shook his hand. Supporters crowded around them. The first day of debates was over.

Tuesday, Dan kicked things off. "It is with great pleasure this morning that we resume our discussion My good brother spent valuable time in his closing speech last night telling you what I believe.

But, not being an expert mind reader, he missed some things. I do believe that all infants are saved in Christ until they forfeit this salvation by sinning…God does not have contradictory ways of saving people. He does not save a baby one way and a grown man a different way…

Now when a lot of intelligent people read the bible and come up with the same conclusion, it is a pretty reasonable surmise that they have not all been mistaken… the bible does really teach that in saving a soul, the Spirit of God operates by direct and immediate impact…"

Boles responded, "The most ignorant people in the world claim direct impact, Dr. Turney can you deny that they are ignorant?"

"Brother Boles," Dan answered, "has collected a great many passages of scripture….No one denies that the power of God is the Gospel, We all teach and preach that the entrance of God's word giveth light but we say that the regenerating work of the Holy Spirit operates by direct or immediate contact….

When God has forgiven a man his sins, will the fellow know it? Not unless God reveals it to him…by the direct impact of the Spirit of God. Without it, there can be no assurance of pardon. I back this up with quite an array of scripture: Galatians 3:2-5, 5:5; Ephesians 2:18, 3:16, 4:3; Ezekiel 36:35-37, etc.

Look at it. Here we have testimony after testimony; volumes of it, oceans of it. All based on the idea that man is not and never can be his own Savior. Until God intervenes, no soul can get remission and regeneration…My brother, if God by his Spirit has never given you assurance of pardon, then according to the word of God, you have never been pardoned…."

Boles, shaking his head, stepped to the podium. "How does God create a clean heart? Doctor Turney says by direct impact. The Bible says through the word. Dr. Turney assumes his position and I show you what the bible says. Any point he can make concerning the Holy Ghost, I can make showing that the Holy Ghost works by the word of God."

They continued sparring. Dan took his turn. "…Unless you are regenerated by the direct impact of the Holy Spirit you are not regenerated at all…Salvation is depended **not** upon your external action, but upon the internal exercise of faith." He concluded, "My brother still did not answer the six arguments I introduced in the first hour."

Boles threw out his own accusation, "Dr. Turney will not explain who or what the Holy Spirit is, but that he works by direct impact. I am compelled to show you how he works…Dr. Turney says he works by direct **impact;** the bible says he **speaks.**"

Back at the podium, Dan spoke, "Brother Boles says that baptism of the Holy Spirit occurred in only two instances, but scriptures do not so state. Paul says, 'For by one Spirit we are all baptized into one body…' Which do you believe, Brother Boles or Paul?"

Boles retorted, "If the Holy Spirit put you into one body, why didn't you stay there? Into one body? He has baptized you into three hundred denominations, all fighting…." That left the crowd laughing and they called it a day.

Wednesday morning, Dan launched into it. "Brother Boles startled me when he said the Holy Spirit never appears but one place at a time. Did you mean that Brother Boles?"

"We have no record of it." Boles replied.

Turney asked, "Did you mean that?"

"Yes, sir."

"This clearly contradicts Psalm 139, John 16:7-14, 2 Cor. 3:17-18, I Cor. 12:13.

His voice took on a mocking tone, "For by the written or spoken word of the Lord, we are all baptized into one body. Uck! Uck!! Uck!!! It doesn't read that way. For by one Bible… Uck! Uck!! Uck!!! It doesn't read that way either. For by one **Spirit** we are all baptized into one body…

Whatever the Holy Spirit does, Christ does; whatever Christ does, the Father does Whatever one does, the others all do. I will illustrate. I take a lighted lamp, now there is one flame, yet there is the light of that flame, the heat of that flame and the burning of that flame. The three are one flame. Take away the light and the heat and the burning would cease; you cannot take away either without taking away all, and yet they are different, but these three are one flame. The Father, the Son and the Holy Ghost are one—God."

Boles shrugged, "What God is above the heavens we know only by the Book." He waved his bible. "Dr. Turney gave you a great deal of gratuitous information on the Godhead...Now I do not speculate on the Godhead. Anything the Book says I will take. I still insist that we are saved by Jesus Christ, saved by the Holy Spirit, saved by God."

Dan's arm swept across the crowd, "Whoever shall call upon the name of the Lord shall be saved. My unsaved friends, if you want to be saved, call upon the name of the Lord. Pray unto him, and he shall hear thee..." He stepped around the podium and stood on the edge of the platform. "I have proven my part of the proposition by plain, direct, positive, unmistakable evidence...that will never be touched. Now Brother Boles and I are traveling toward the Judgement Seat as rapidly as the wheel of time shall revolve, and I want you to be with me..."

"Amen!" Boles responded. A scattering of amens echoed in the room.

Boles thanked the crowd. "Dr. Turney may be done, but I'm not finished yet. You cannot call upon him unless you are a believer." Boles attacked several of Turney's positions and retold a version of the prodigal son to make his point.

Daniel responded, "I have something special for you tonight. It is a new parable of the Prodigal Son. It supports Brother Boles and his theology. You can understand as I read. Now don't say Uck, Uck, Uck too soon, but listen to this divine revelation:

'He arose and came to his father. But when he was a great way off his father saw him, and ordered him to stay back and wait until his brother dunked him in the frog pond before the old man would let him enter the house. The son cried out, 'Father, I have sinned against heaven and in thy sight, and am no longer worthy to be called thy son.' But the father said, 'Not a word further until you have been dunked, and everything that you say to me before that dunking I shall take as a personal affront. I would have you know that confessing and praying before you have been dunked gains no favor in this house.' And he said to the servant, 'If that young man does not come to me by being dunked in the frog pond, he will never taste a slice of the fatted calf...'

That is the most peculiar scripture I ever read in my life! It does service to Brother Bole's idea that you have to be baptized before you can be welcomed home."

The debaters each made another speech. Dan concluded, "I want to thank all of you most sincerely for the close attention you have paid to us in this discussion...May God bless every man, every woman and give us understanding of the truth as it is in Christ Jesus, that at last if we pass away from this world, we may, in the triumphs of a living faith and washed in the blood of the lamb, pass through the gates of the New Jerusalem into Paradise."

Marion Boles concluded by claiming victory in the debate. "You have been very kind to us in listening through this discussion and while we may differ, we are still friends...." The crowd applauded them as the two gave each other bear hugs. Boles whispered, "I already have an idea for our next debate."

Dan said, "Send me your proposition. Until we debate again, safe travels, brother!" Dan hurried to catch the last train to Decatur.

CHAPTER TWENTY-FIVE

Decatur, Illinois
March 1909

When he got home, Dan regaled the family with stories from the debate with Boles. They especially liked his retelling Jesus' parable of the prodigal son. Maggie teased, "There were two brothers in the story, where is the sister?"

Emma answered, "Probably in the kitchen cooking the fatted calf."

"I'm glad the father welcomed his youngest son back home," George chimed in. "But, Dad, the Turney version of the story should portray the father as the one who is always be gone!"

"Prodigal father," Maggie said.

"I'm a polemic, not a prodigal," Dan answered.

Emma asked, "How soon before you travel off to another far country?"

"I'm going to Ohio, next week," he admitted.

"Where?" George asked.

"Preaching in Empire, then debating in Wellsville."

"Another week-long venture?" Emma lamented.

"At least. But I have to be back in Illinois for district meetings April 5 in Clark County.

"Before you board the next train, you better read Bertha's letter!" Emma implored, pulling it from a stack on the table.

"It's from Bertha and not John?"

"Yes. Read it yourself, it's not good," Emma said.

Dan took the letter and scanned it. "Something's wrong with John?"

"Evidently. They've already seen several doctors," Emma said.

"John doesn't want us to know?" Dan asked.

"So it seems," George replied.

Dan kept busy, running from church meetings to debates to political gatherings. He worked with Bill Boles to organize a new political party in Illinois. By April, they identified followers in 17 states. Worries about John plagued Emma. She dreaded each day's mail. She sent John two newspaper articles about Dan, hoping he'd respond. It worked. John replied, commenting on his dad's fascination with airships and his scheme to raise money by going door-to-door.

"Dad is brighter than the best
And sillier than all the rest
My mother always knows best
So I ask, can your eldest pass his test?"

She scribbled a quick replied, inquiring about the 'test'. "Are you ill? I beg you, tell us!"

Emma fretted until John replied. Then she wept. When Dan got home, she cried out, "John has tuberculosis!!"

He was jolted. After much talking and praying, they knew they had to go see John in Toledo. Dan made arrangements and they caught the train to Iowa. It was a bitter homecoming back to central Iowa. Dan was in a stupor. Years of scholarly research gave him no answers. He kicked his big bag of precious books. They lay silently at his feet. Emma squeezed his hand, which lay limp in his lap.

Daughter-in-law Bertha met them at the Marshalltown station. After the buggy ride to Toledo, she led them into the house. It smelled of medicines and sadness. John, bedridden, tried to sit up and greet them, but coughed instead. Emma rushed to his side, hugging him as only a mother could.

They spent a month with John and Bertha. John recuperated under their attention. Father and son rekindled their love of linguistics and the classics. John was especially interested in the Greek New Testament. The pair parsed Greek verbs and would have spoken to each other in Greek, had it been a living language.

Emma asked Bertha, "Have you ever known such a scholarly father and son?"

Bertha said, "It's so good to see them study together. John has his father's love of words." Her voice broke. "Emma, I love your son, so much, so very much!" The women embraced. The men, in the bedroom, were lost in their world of words.

Before they left Toledo, Bertha confided "I'm making arrangements to take John to Arizona. Phoenix has a climate that offers recovery for some tuberculosis sufferers. There are fine doctors there. I want John to get the best care possible." Dan and Emma agreed. The goodbyes were poignant. Dan told John, "Keep up your study of Greek. We will talk again, when you get back to the Midwest. Meanwhile, send me your notes. Maybe they'll help my preaching."

Dan thought of John the next time he preached. He was presenting an open- air sermon in Decatur's Central Park. A small crowd gathered. Coins and a few bills were tossed into Dan's old hat during the offering. Emma said, "Almost enough to buy your coffee this week." Dan wished he had money enough to help John and Bertha out in Arizona.

That fall, Dan was both Conference President and Polemic; two jobs, with half-a-paycheck. He spent many weeks preaching his way back and forth across southern Illinois. He got home to Decatur and spent a sober Thanksgiving with George and Maggie. He put two empty chairs up to the table, "To remind us of John E.Z. and Bertha."

"As if we could ever stop thinking of them," Emma said.

When they had cleared the table, Dan spread out John's recent letters. "He has been translating the Greek New Testament into Esperanto. He's almost half-way through the Gospel of John. Sibling rivalry flared in George's eyes, "I doubt he'll bother to translate the Gospel of George."

Maggie said, "There's no Gospel of George, silly."

"Maybe, I should write one!" George answered.

"Enough church talk," Emma said. "How about some pumpkin pie?"

"It was a good year for pumpkins," Maggie said.

George said, "Before we have Mom's delicious pie, tell me more about this Esperanto language John is using."

Emma shook her head when Dan launched scholarly lecture #557, "George, it's an international language created by Polish scholar L.L. Zamenhof in 1887. I gave John my copy of the text before we left Toledo. It's based on Latin and is catching on all over the world."

John E.Z. Turney's scholarly notes were pushed aside when Emma walked in with plates of pumpkin pie. "I don't have enough to feed the 4,000, but I have enough for the four of us." Lost in the pie, they spoke no more of Esperanto.

On December 14, they got a terse, heart-rending telegram from Phoenix, "John E.Z. Turney died today!" A few days later, they got a letter from Bertha describing the funeral service and the burial in Greenwood Cemetery. Daniel immediately sat down and wrote an obituary highlighting John's life. He sent copies to towns where his son had lived. He told the family, "It's my way of honoring him!"

Before Christmas, they received a large envelope from the widow. Emma opened it and pulled out dozens of pages: J.E.Z.'s death certificate, a short newspaper obituary, a few copies of John's poems and his last translation of the Gospel of John into Esperanto. George observed, "His handwriting got wobblier toward the end."

Maggie pushed away from the table, "I don't want to think about it."

Dan couldn't put the pages down. "He didn't give up. John kept working on this, right up to the end." He flipped through the pages until he got to the last one. The writing was shaky, but he could still read it, "*Jesuo diris al sxi:Mi estas la revelvigxo kaj la vivo; kiu kredas al mi, ecx se li estos mortinta, tiu vivos.*"

"What does it mean?" George asked.

"It's John 11:25 where Jesus tells Martha, 'I am the resurrection. and the life: he that believeth in me, though he were dead, yet shall he live."

Emma said, "I don't know whether to sing or cry. Dan, that's your favorite funeral text."

"Resurrection! Easter!" George exclaimed.

"Those were the last words he wrote!" Dan touched the paper, as if it was a sacred relic. "It's a message from John to us!"

Emma lifted her hands. "It's also a message from the Lord!"

1910

The Turneys plodded through winter's snow dragging their personal griefs. They knew spring had finally come when George announced, "I saw turkey vultures floating in the sky and heard robins singing in the meadow." Dan got an additional job as a 1910 census enumerator and went door-to-door collecting data. He finished his survey of the west side of Decatur's 4th ward in early May. His legs complained, but Emma celebrated, "Our cupboards are no longer quite so bare!"

In mid-May, as Methodist Protestant Conference president, Dan started his two-month tour of local churches. His small salary and a few offerings barely covered his train fares. He slept in borrowed beds and his food was free, courtesy of covered dish potlucks and parsonage hospitality. While Turney wore his preacher's hat, political buddies were touting him as a future presidential candidate. He was still unknown nationally. The *Topeka Daily Capital* asked, "Who is Daniel Braxton Turney?"

Daniel took a positive step and mended fences with William R. Benkert, the powerhouse of his old United Christian political party. Emma had convinced him over a cup of coffee one night, "Dan, you preach that we are a forgiven people and we ought to forgive. Practice what you preach." Chided into action, he wrote an apology letter. Benkert's positive reply came just as Dan was heading down to Cowden, Illinois for another baptism debate.

1911

Emma kissed him goodbye, "I'll be glad to have you back home." She watched him cinch up his coat and step into the January cold.

When he returned nine days later, it was even colder. A debate with Chicago socialist E.E. Carr promised to heat things up. George told his mother, "Dad is willing to debate anybody about anything! And he usually wins!"

"So, he tells us!" Emma smiled

Dan got into a debate with chairman Benkert about whether the United Christian party should be renamed as the American Party or the Christian Patriot Party. That argument continued into the May 1st national party meeting in Rock Island, Illinois. Some thought they would lose support if they changed the party's name. Others argued that a name change might help more than hurt. The convention couldn't decide which name to use, but agreed that Daniel B. Turney and Samuel C. Carter should be their presidential and vice-presidential candidates.

On July 1, 1911 Daniel B. Turney again launched his campaign in Mt. Vernon, Illinois. This time he did his groundwork and was greeted by a crowd of 1,000. He modeled his kick-off after his grandfather Braxton Parish's big political event back in 1864. He duplicated Parish's techniques, right down to the marching bands and the states being represented by 46 young women dressed in red sashes, white waists and blue skirts, honoring the national colors. Dan told Emma, "It was a resounding success. Remember, my grandpa never lost an election!" She bit her tongue to keep from saying, "And you've never won one." Instead she spoke a different truth, "Grandpa Parish is a fine model to copy!"

Dan made few political speeches that fall, but got quoted saying, "The United Christians intend to sweep the Republicans and the Democrats and the Mormons and the Catholics out of the United States into Japan, Canada, Australia, Switzerland or some other equally inaccessible place." Dan complained, "I only get quoted when the reporters think I've said something crazy."

Emma replied, "Remember in the last election, how they kept quoting your comment about 'the extravagance of monarch-cursed kingdoms' and your plan to cut the president's salary in half?"

"They kept running it. But, I'm still an unknown. Maybe bad quotes are better than none at all!"

1912

D. B. Turney couldn't seem to get any rhythm to his presidential campaign. Illinois newspapers ignored him and he couldn't afford to travel to Tennessee or Ohio to speak.

He unloaded his frustration on George one night. His son's answer stunned him, "Dad, I've got more important things on my mind."

"More important than the presidency of the United States?"

"Yes! I told you I've taken a shine to a young woman I met at work. It's serious. Edlyn Sleeter and I are going to get married!" George was 31 years old and his parents had almost given up on his ever marrying.

"Congratulations, son! Emma, come in here! George has an important announcement." She was elated. "When do we get to meet this lucky woman?"

That weekend, George introduced them to Edlyn. She was a shy bookkeeper and former school teacher, the oldest in her family of seven siblings. They were glad she came from a strong Methodist family. Edlyn told them, "My grandfather Jockisch started the German Methodist Church in Boody. It's a little village south of Decatur."

Emma was obsessed with the June wedding, but Dan sharpened his focus on the upcoming election. Two of his promotional letters had stirred a little national interest. Presidential candidate D.B. Turney headed for the city library to do some research on his opponents. He was ready to pull open the door when he was assailed by T.N. Crews, a gadfly reporter for the *Decatur Herald*. Crews waved a copy of the March 12th issue of the *New York Sun* in Dan's face. "Did you see this, Turney?" His finger tapped the headline **Turney Triumphs-Beats Roosevelt!**

Dan was flabbergasted.

"You are becoming nationally famous, Turney. Can I get a quote for tomorrow's edition?"

Dan grabbed the paper, "What's this about?"

"They did a poll of descendants of signers of the Declaration of Independence and asked who they'd choose for president. Guess what? You topped the list with 144,007 votes. Roosevelt got only 141 votes."

"That's too good to be true!" Daniel exclaimed.

"My thought exactly!" Crews replied. "Did you fabricate the article?"

"I did not! But, like you, I'm not sure I believe it to be true. Although I am a great-great grandson of Carter Braxton of Virginia, a signer of the Declaration."

"Can I quote you on that?"

"You can! Sorry, Mr. Crews, I have to go check out some books." Dan had trouble concentrating as he walked through the library. 'Who could have made up such a story?'

A month later, Crews sat in his cubicle at the *Decatur Review* and heard his named called out from the lobby. "Crews. T.N. Crews. I need to talk with you!" It was his favorite preacher-politician-wanna-be, Daniel B. Turney. A red-faced Turney rushed to his desk. "I'm being slighted and trivialized!"

"What are you talking about?" Crews asked.

"Teddy Roosevelt will be at Power's Opera House today. I deserve to be on that stage with him. I couldn't even get to the stage door!"

"Why don't you just go to the front door?"

Indignant, Turney said, "I wouldn't walk around the block to hear him unless I can have a seat on the stage with the other dignitaries. As a national presidential candidate, I am entitled to that courtesy!"

Crews replied, "You have a point, sir. You are Decatur's only candidate. You ought to be up front."

"Are you mocking me?" Dan huffed.

"No! In fact, I'm on my way over to the Opera House right now." Pointing to the press pass hanging around his neck, Crews said, "I'll use my influence to get you that stage seat ticket. Let's go!" They walked over together. Crews left Turney at the stage door, "I'll see what I can do." Crews, waving his credentials, threaded through the crowd. When he finally got the precious ticket, he couldn't find Turney. It took Crews ten minutes to spot Decatur's candidate, hidden in the mass of ticketless humanity at the stage entrance.

"Thank you! Thank you!!" Turney said as he dashed for the stage door. Crews followed him through the doorway and joined the other 2,573 political fans who were jammed into the opera house. Dan proudly headed for the stage as Crews elbowed his way into the throng filling the outside aisle. They waited for the former president who was on a one-day whistle-stop campaign tour across Illinois to Indiana. Theodore Roosevelt was making nine appearances and nine brief stump speeches. D.B. Turney sat proudly on stage and listened to Teddy's Decatur rendition.

In May, Dan claimed his own moment in the sun when he joined the crowd of delegates at the United Christian Party convention in Illinois. The assembled in Rock Island's Watch Tower Park, high above the Rock River. Daniel was on center stage. The moderator spoke in serious tones, "We have named our candidates- clean, capable and worthy men. For President, Daniel B. Turney of Decatur, Illinois, a great-great-grandson of Carter Braxton of Virginia, one of the signers of the Declaration of Independence." The crowd cheered and clapped until candidate Turney stood and waved. The speaker continued, "And for vice president, Samuel C. Carter of Howard Lake, Minnesota. These men are ready to render immediate and efficient support for the cause of right.

We ask for Turney and Carter, the support of all persons in accord with this platform-

'Truth crushed to earth will rise again

The eternal years of God are here....'"

When the convention ended, Turney and Carter crossed the The Mississippi River into Davenport for a press conference at The *Quad City Times'* auditorium. A handful of reporters asked enough questions to almost make Dan miss his train.

Candidate Turney was totally exhausted when he got home late Saturday night. "Em, I don't know how Roosevelt managed nine appearances in a single day." She tucked him into bed.

"Just be glad you're a Turney, not a Roosevelt!"

The next day, after regaining his strength, he gave her a full report. "There were 250 delegates from seven states. That's a 5,000 percent increase over last time."

Emma poured him another cup of coffee, "Don't get your hopes up too high. I'm not sure this country is ready to live by the Golden Rule!

When you get back from your interview with Crews at the *Review*, George wants to talk about housing plans after he and Edlyn marry."

"They aren't moving in with us are they?"

"I'll let George tell you."

That night, when he got home from the post office, George told him. Dan responded, "You are marrying into wealth! Edlyn's father is really going to build you a new house while you are honeymooning in California?"

"He is. It will be a two-story house on 1033 S. Maffit Street! But I consider the Sleeters more industrious than rich."

"Does Mr. Sleeter have that much lumber?"

"He better," George said. "Remember, the wedding is next month!"

Maggie was happy for George, but told her mother, "I'm feeling a wee bit jealous!"

June 14 came quickly. They watched George Joseph Turney marry Edlyn Louisa Amelia Sleeter. It was a family-only celebration. After posing for wedding photos, Emma whispered, "Edlyn sure has a big family!"

"They are a talkative bunch!" Dan said.

"The pot calling the kettle black."

Dan shrugged, "Well, they are Methodist folks, even though some have heavy German accents. Guess we could attend their church, but wouldn't fit in too well since the service is in German."

"That is one of your languages isn't it, Dr. Turney?"

He gave her arm a squeeze, "Yes, it is! I understand Edlyn's grandmother Jockisch doesn't speak a word of English."

"I reckon her English is better than my German!" Emma said.

George and Edlyn headed for California on their honeymoon. Dan hit the summer campaign trail. Carpenter C.W. Sleeter built the newlywed's house faster than D.B. Turney could build his campaign. Sleeter finished his task by hanging a bright new swing on the porch; Turney had to quit campaigning and put on his preacher's hat to begin his sweep across southern Illinois to visit his 70 plus M.P. churches. One night, he jotted a note to Emma, "Maybe I couldn't do

Roosevelt's nine campaign stops, but I'm not sure he could do the church stumping I do every fall."

Emma smiled and told Maggie, "Your father is feeling better about himself."

"I think he's happier as a preacher than he is as a politician," Maggie said.

A few weeks after Dan returned to Decatur, election day rolled around. Dan met George at the polling site and they stepped into adjoining voting booths. George whispered through the thin curtain, "Dad, I can't find you on the ballot!"

D.B. Turney bellowed back, "Benkert failed me again. We didn't even make the Illinois ballot!" The United Christian party had missed all 48 state deadlines and got no votes. Woodrow Wilson won the election handily.

Later that day, a newspaper reporter and camera man stopped by the Turney cottage. Dan posed for a formal photo, while Emma scrubbed clothes in the backyard. The photographer asked him why he wasn't helping. Dan said, "I carried the wash water from the well. Our daughter will be home soon to help her hang the clothes." The reporter shook his head, "Here, I thought you were a true suffragist! Why don't we pose that picture again, with your wife in the background?"

Dan refused and stomped back into the house, just as Maggie got home. She helped hang the wash. "Mom, I got the job!"

"In Washington, D.C.?" Emma asked.

"I'll be a filing clerk at the Department of Agriculture!"

CHAPTER TWENTY-SIX

Washington, D.C.
1913-1914

When Emma told Dan, he blurted out, "Why don't we go with her. I can be a polemic again in the U.S. Capital. We can live in D.C., even if I didn't get elected president." Emma did not want to move but had reservations about Maggie, a single woman, going off to the big city by herself. Emma eventually agreed.

They found a place to live in D.C.; 112 2nd Street, NE was close to the Department of Agriculture building. Maggie began training for her new job. Dan dabbled in various research projects. He wrote back to the *Decatur Herald* and advertised his availability, "I am engaged in special research here in the Library of Congress. My charges are 50 cents per hour. One of my patrons wanted to know just when the fifth year of Meiji ended and the sixth year started. In half an hour, I found in French, German and English that it corresponded to Jan. 1, 1873. So, if there be anything needing special research that can be unearthed by documents, manuscripts or books in the Library of Congress, my services can be secured. Rates reasonable and satisfactory work guaranteed...." The article produced a few research requests. But that didn't keep Dan's mind occupied. He was obsessed with writing his latest book, which he called *Consolidated, Condensed, Conelliated*

Chronology. He tried to explain it to Emma, "I'm exploring different methods of calculating time, using ancient calendars and harmonizing them with the chronology of the bible. The first edition will cost about $1,000. But don't worry, I plan to raise $1,500 of subscriptions before I publish."

That fall, while Emma stayed behind to support Maggie, Dan went back to Illinois to promote his book and attend the M.P. Annual Conference. At the meeting in Goreville, Dan was elected first president of the board of church extension, chairman of the standing committee and the conference faculty of examination." An old friend teased, "You just got yourself a lot of titles and work and no pay." Dan met with his committees, guest preached and pitched his book to anyone who would listen. Some were befuddled by his book idea; most were indifferent; a few were intrigued; but no one offered funding.

He returned to D.C. with empty pockets, but unfazed hopes. Emma shook her head, "You never give up!" But Maggie did. After 16 months, she quit her clerk's job.

She admitted, "I'm just not cut out for this."

Emma told them both, "It's time to go back to Decatur. Dan, you can do your church work better there." He didn't disagree. D.C. was too far for a commute.

"Where will we live when we get back to Decatur?" Maggie asked

"We can ask to stay with George and Edlyn until we find a house," Emma suggested. In two weeks, they'd made arrangements to stay with George and bought 3 train tickets. They were on the road again.

CHAPTER TWENTY-SEVEN

Decatur, Illinois
1915

During their brief stay with George, his wife Edlyn told Emma, "We are expecting our first child in June!" George helped them find a new, smaller home. Emma was relieved to have their own place. She told Dan, "We can't burden them with our money troubles. They have their own issues and things won't get easier after the baby comes."

Grandson Donald M. Turney was born June 4, 1915. Emma was so excited she couldn't remember what she was going to fix for supper. "I've been blessed with another grandson!" Dan shared her joy.

Maggie stopped by 1033 Maffit Street after work and peeked in on her new nephew. When she got home, she found her father shuffling through old copies of the *Methodist Reporter*. Maggie asked, "Are you saving your articles for little Donald when he learns to read?"

Emma, who knew about reading to children, said, "Your father's circumlocution wasn't written for a boy just learning to read; better wait until he finishes college."

Dan ignored them and focused on unfolding the Oct. 17, 1914 issue. He found the paragraph he was looking for. "I hope when Donald M. Turney is a grown man that he will know the atoning work of Jesus Christ."

"I agree, Dr. Turney! If I remember correctly, you wrote twelve articles on that subject last year, didn't you?" Em said.

"I did. It's a critical theological subject. Here's my favorite line on page 7 of the last article, "To Jesus Christ only may we turn for life, for joy, for love, not allowing ourselves to brood over what we are powerless to remedy and by putting our trust in him, we may go forward....confidently in the atoning work of Jesus Christ.""

Maggie said, "I like the idea of not brooding, but putting our trust in the Lord."

Emma added, "We mustn't brood about baby Donald...."

"But trust him to the Lord," Dan finished her sentence.

That trust was tested by Donald's slowness to walk or talk. Dan reminded the family, "I didn't talk until I after I was two."

Emma smiled and withheld saying, "And you've been talking constantly ever since!" Sometimes they finished each other's sentences and usually she knew when not to.

As toddler Donald was learning to walk, baby sister Lois Iola was born March 1, 1917. D.B. Turney missed her birth. He was in Allentown Michigan debating against Latter Day Saints. He was so pumped up by the two-week debate that he went to the newspaper office before visiting granddaughter Lois. When the editorial staff questioned Turney about his debates, he said, "I am always willing to attack dangerous error and to defend wholesome truth."

Five weeks later, Dan and Emma made their weekly trek to see baby Lois. Dan would never forget opening the paper and reading that congress had voted to enter the battlefields of World War I. Baby Lois was crying and Dan reflected, "Lois Iola, we're joining that bloody war in France. There will be crying in homes all across the land." Edlyn tried to comfort Lois's colic, without ignoring Donald tugging on her dress. Edlyn's sisters Lilly and Bertha helped in the kitchen until George got home from the post office.

Dan was not comfortable with children in general and was very awkward with them before they could talk. Lois, unlike Donald, was quick to walk and even quicker to talk. Emma said, "At the rate she's going, she will read before Donald does!" Emma doted on the two, as often as she could.

1920

D.B. Turney, who had been S. Illinois delegate to General Conferences in Ohio in 1916, went again to North Carolina in 1920. Some national leaders remembered him from his days as denominational polemic. Dan insisted, "I'm still a polemic! I just did a baptismal debate down in Big Clifty, Kentucky with a doctor from Florida. In a few weeks I'll be debating my old friend Marion Boles down in Mt Vernon, Illinois.

The Kentucky representative said, "I've never heard of Big Clifty?"

"No surprise," Dan said. It's a tiny place in Grayson County, north of Bowling Green. We had good crowds for eight days!" But times were changing, Dan was aging and his debate days were ending. He also stepped back from politics, writing the *Decatur Herald*, "The presidential bee has ceased buzzing in my bonnet...thanks...to everyone who has made mention of my name."

That fall, Emma joined Dan at the presidential election polling place. She was excited. Voting was a new thing for her. She leaned on her husband, "Dan, all those years you worked for the cause of suffrage. You helped this happen! I can vote." They cast their ballots on Nov. 2, 1920. Warren G. Harding won handily.

Dan said, "Guess the republicans didn't need me as a candidate; they did well in nominating Harding."

Dan's energy was lagging, as was Emma's. He was retired and no longer received a church salary. The Methodist Protestants had no pension plan. Invitations to speak were dwindling and his debate days were over.

"Dan, how are we going to get by?" Emma asked. She had become more of a worrier as the years passed. Dan wrote old friends and begged for speaking engagements. Most were too busy to even answer his letters. He unloaded on George, who was starting a part-time printing business in their house on Maffit Street. Edlyn helped set type when the children napped.

George gave his father some money to tide them over. Dan offered to pay him back. "No, Dad. I'll help when I can." Edlyn clenched her fists in disapproval and stomped out of the room. George confessed, "Dad, I just can't sleep. I toss and turn for an hour or two, then get up and piddle around in the print shop. I need three cups of coffee to help me go to work at the post office. I come home. The kids are fussy. Edlyn and I argue. I go to work in the print shop and work until I'm exhausted. I still can't sleep. I drink more coffee and stumble back to the post office. I don't know how long I can keep this up!"

Dan didn't know what to say, so he walked home. He could hear George and Edlyn fighting before he got to the corner. He helped Emma in the garden, realizing how much he had taken her for granted.

While at George's, he'd noticed a stack of flyers about a door-to-door company called Zanol. Dan thought about his years of traveling and meeting strangers. 'I could sell.' He contacted the company and ordered a starter kit. He was soon clumping down Decatur's street with a bag of samples hanging from his left shoulder in his old travel bag. His new bag was crammed, not with ideas and history, but with soaps, liniments, household gadgets and magic cures. He didn't really believe in most of them, but had to sell to survive. They couldn't manage on Emma's garden and handouts.

He climbed up the steps to another porch and knocked. The housewife who answered was not interested. It did not matter that he'd helped her get the right to vote and made it harder for her husband to get drunk. Slam! So, it went. Some people peeked through the curtains and spotted him coming up the sidewalk, then ignored his knock. A few listened to his spiel and bought some soap or powders. He trudged home, wishing he had a church to preach to. He often thought of George and his struggle to sleep. 'I know how it feels when the mind acts like a runaway horse, crazy and out-of-control. A poem began to form in the peddler's mind and he morphed back into a writer.

"Why do we Sleep?" Verse after verse poured out. Dan stayed awake until had written them down.

"For while we sleep, as God sees best,

183

He tunes our ears to his request,
And draws us back from doubt and fear,
And makes his mercies very clear…
We sleeping grow in psychic store,
Our deeper selves our lamps explore…
By will of him who made us so,
We sleep to dream and see and know,
Where God doth rule, where love doth reign,
Where joy is found unmix'd with pain…."

When he finished, Dan slept peacefully. The next morning, he showed the poem to Emma. "Dan that's seventeen verses long. It will take all morning to read. When she finished, Emma said, "Give it to George. I pray it helps him!"

George appreciated his father's thoughts, but continued to be plagued with emotional pain and sleeplessness. He prowled Decatur's streets by night seeking elusive peace; his father plodded the streets by day seeking sales. Both were trying to survive.

That routine lasted for months, but was broken when they got word that Emma's eighty-nine-year-old step-mother died. The burial was set for April 6, down in Emma's home town of Richview. She admitted, "I just don't have the gumption to travel that far, but I don't want to disrespect her."

"I can go for you, for us," Dan said. "Your family treated us well and deserves our respect." Traveling south, Dan thought about his first trip to Richview, when he asked Rev. Daniel Ogelsby for Emma's hand in marriage. Ogelsby buried two wives before dying twelve years ago. Dan wondered if all three wives would be buried beside him. It made him feel old and ponder things too deep for words. In two-weeks he would be 75. His bones ached. He hoped Emma was doing better. She had fallen and broken her wrist, insisting that he tape up her hand, "Dan, we can't afford a doctor." Sometimes he wondered if it was the **lack** of money and not the **love** of money that was the root of all evil.

As his birthday neared, he became more reflective, almost morose. He repeatedly unfolded and reread the yellowed letter from his younger brother out in California:

"We are drifting along the river of time, dear Brother, and there are autumn leaves along the shore and floating on the stream along here; farther along they will become more numerous. Still, I have the spirt of a boy, and am as interested in boyish things as I ever was. When Paul became a man, he put away childish things; this being one of the respects, along with many others, in which I am not like him. Lily Baxter and I have had our joys and sorrows together, and we love each other a great deal better now than we did at first. Unless poverty or bad health embitter life for us, I look for us to have the finest and happiest part of our life in the part that remains…. -Leander."

Dan wanted to believe that the happiest part of life was yet to come. He slowly refolded the letter with his arthritic hands. Emma blamed his arthritis on too much writing and too many big books. She was probably right. Books brought them together and his love of his tomes often kept them apart. 'Do I love books and languages more than I love people? That's not right. Christ Jesus died for humanity, not for books.' He thought about getting a book from his sagging shelves, but instead leaned back in his chair and took a little rest.

On his birthday, twenty-two friends from Illinois, Arizona, Ohio, Indiana and Iowa, surprised him with a dollar shower. Emma opened the last envelope, "We may have enough to buy you some coffee!" It was a happy day.

1923

But son George was not happy. He was troubled, agitated, disturbed! Neither Dan nor Emma could name his affliction. His not sleeping escalated into all-night prowling through the dark streets of Decatur.

On May 12, they were jolted awake by a frantic rap on their front door. Lilly, Edlyn's sister, hesitated before blurting, "They've taken George!"

"Taken him where?"

"To Jacksonville. He's been committed!" Jacksonville's State Hospital treated mental disorders. No family wanted a loved one to go there. It was a shame on the family name.

"I'm sorry," Lilly said. "Edlyn couldn't take it any longer!"

After she left, Emma wept. "Dan, I don't know if I can take this!" He held her, unwilling to regurgitate empty words of consolation.

Months dragged by. Emma and Dan helped Edlyn put up her garden produce. Dan set type for printing jobs. Six-year-old Lois stared up at them with searching eyes, "When is my daddy coming home?" Dan tried to distract them all from that question by taking the children to the sandbox George had built during better days. After Lois calmed down, Dan took Donald into the yard to play catch. They lost the ball in a pile of leaves next to the picket fence. Lois joined them in the search.

On November 16, George returned home, gaunt and silent. Six months had passed, but he'd aged ten years. At first, only daughter Lois could put a light in his eyes. The two had a special bond. She eagerly sat in his lap and read her latest book. George quit his job at the post office. He couldn't face coworkers who knew he had been in the crazy house. He told his parents, "Edlyn and I will have to make our living with the Turney Printing Company. She has quick hands. Together, we can do more print jobs.

George seldom talked about the six-month Jacksonville gap in his life. One day, he opened up, admitting to the horror of electric shock, shackles and drug experiments.

The City of Decatur prospered and the Turney printing business grew. But there was no regular paycheck. Emma said, "Living off a printing business is a little like our living off your debates." George's life grew back to normalcy, including regular vocal bouts with Edlyn. One night at supper, an especially feisty Lois told her parents. "Stop fighting. Act like adults!" The family started attending church again and began taking walks on Sunday afternoons. These long walks took them to farm roads, city parks and railroad tracks. They picked berries, collected leaves and bugs and found some peace."

Emma told Dan, "I wish I could walk with them on Sundays."

"It's given them a dose of tranquility," he agreed. "I get all the walking I can take on my Zanol sales route!"

"And you had to do most of our gardening this year."

"It makes me stronger to play ball with Donald."

She said, "He likes playing with you!"

"George is becoming a baseball fan, too. He Listens to the St. Louis Cardinal games while they work in the print shop. Hope we can save up a few pennies to go see a ball game here in Decatur."

Emma saved every penny they got in change and put them in her secret ball game jar. She wanted her boys to be able to enjoy a ball game together. It took her months of penny pinching to get tickets. Husband Dan, son George and grandson Donald were elated. Donald kept singing, "Take me out to the ballgame!" The day came and they were not disappointed. When they got home, Donald begged her, "Save more pennies!" He gave her a small handful of coins from his piggy bank.

But Emma's focus shifted. Daniel B. Turney's health was failing. They needed all their pennies for groceries and medicines. Something was seriously wrong. A doctor finally gave Emma a diagnosis, "It is liver cancer. There's not much we can do except try to keep him comfortable."

Emma responded, "Dan and I have been blessed with 50 years of marriage., some better, some worse, few richer and mostly poorer." The doctor nodded. He knew she was a battle-hardened marriage veteran.

Fall 1925

George stopped by and asked Emma, "Is Dad always this tired?"

She admitted, "He takes long morning and afternoon naps. He's not doing well."

"I'd like to pep him up, get his mind off his sickness. How about I take him out to a ballgame?" Emma agreed. George said, "I'll get tickets. We'll take Donald along and make it a memorable outing."

Two days later, the three of them took the streetcar to the nearest baseball park. Ten-year-old Donald wanted to sit up front, close to the action. Dan didn't care, as long as there were not too many bleacher steps to climb. He sat between his son and grandson and munched on peanuts. They had splurged with a treat. In the 6th inning, Dan was distracted by a noisy group of students and took his eyes off the batter's box. They heard the bat crack and the foul ball curved toward the crowd. The ball smacked Dan's head and he collapsed, never seeing it bounce back on to the field. George and Donald wrestled the 78-year-old back into a sitting position. He was dazed and his glasses were askew. George knew they had to leave immediately and get his father home. They wobbled back to the streetcar stop. Donald whined, "Why do we have to leave. Grandpa should have kept his eye on the ball!" The old man was accused and confused. His son was worried.

When they got Dan home, George apologized, "Mom, I'm so sorry!" He helped her put him to bed. The ball injury was a downward turning point in his health battle. Dan often spent the day in bed and some days didn't even open a book. One side of his bed sagged from their weight. He'd ask Emma for a specific volume and then not have the strength to read it. Emma left the stack there, hoping her book-lover would come back to life.

It happened, just before Christmas. A visit from Donald and Lois perked him up. Then he got a letter from his old preacher friend Amsbury Reynolds. It got his intellectual and spiritual juices pumping. He opened his bible, flipped through, making the connection between passages. The old spark was back. He asked for writing paper and a pen. For a while, he tried to write propped up in the bed. Then, with Emma's help, he hobbled over to his desk, brushed off the dust and sat down.

"Thoughts are racing through my mind. I've got to corral them before they escape." He scratched and scribbled, crossed out and rewrote. Emma rejoiced to see her strange genius resurrected. "Em, come here. Let me read this to you!" She scooted a kitchen chair up next to his desk. He began reading:

"I still live, with the strong desire to be of service in the great cause of the Lord Jesus Christ, and to round out my life's influence so that it will be an ever-working force for Christianity.

Glad indeed am I that God has made it possible for progress to be along the time of suffering, and that the spirit may have great consolation, even while the body feels much pain. And I wish my brethren in the Methodist Protestant Church to put me in their prayers, and not to lose sight of the fact that the sufferers in the world have often been its benefactors. Let no present affliction hinder such usefulness as is in our power. Let us give roses though we touch thorns.

Death conducts judgment and one who comes through judgment with Christ, finds home, the real home."

Later, Emma told George, "It was like he was birthing a baby. He had to get those words out and write them down. I mailed his letter to Rev. Reynolds."

"How is Dad doing, now?"

"As exhausted as a woman after a long labor. He's back in his bed, sleeping most of the time."

D. B. Turney's strength continued ebbing away. Emma moved his reading books off the bed. He couldn't use them and they got in her way in caring for him. It got harder every day. George came by to help her turn him over. In the second week of January, he went into a coma and never woke up. He died January 18, 1926. The day after he died, Rev. Reynold's response letter arrived,

January 16, 1926

"Dear Dan,

Received your letter, just after the holidays. I was touched by your challenge for us to give roses, even though we touch thorns. What an image for our 53-year journey together through life!

Dan, you have been a profound scholar, brilliant logician and an eloquent defender of the faith. I consider you one of the most gifted polemics of our age and an unsurpassed genius in doctrinal controversy. Your fruitful pen has left a noble testimony to your greatness of mind and heart. But above all these, you are my friend.

I treasure the end of your letter. It was a delightful, lingering echo from the border-land: 'Yes, I have spiritual sustenance amidst my intense sufferings, and my sky of hope is unclouded by doubt and filled with golden glory through the assurance of faith in Jesus Christ.'

Amsbury L. Reynolds"

Daniel Braxton Turney was buried 20 January 1926 in Boiling Springs Cemetery (also called Graceland Cemetery), Hickory Township, Macon County, Decatur, Illinois.

THE
METHODIST
RECORDER

Vol. LXXXVII.   PITTSBURGH, PA., FEBRUARY 27, 1926.   Number 9.

DANIEL BRAXTON TURNEY.—1848-1926.

In the midst of the bodily sufferings of his last days, and with a courageous and unfaltering faith which welcomed even his afflictions as mysterious messengers of God for his greater final good, Dr. Turney penned the following words of farewell to the Methodist Protestant Church:

"I still live, with the strong desire to be of service in the great cause of the Lord Jesus Christ, and to round out my life's influence so that it will be an ever working force for Christianity.

"Glad indeed am I that God has made it possible for progress to be along the line of suffering, and that the spirit may have great consolation, even while the body feels much pain. And I wish my brethren in the Methodist Protestant Church to put me in their prayers, and not to lose sight of the fact that the sufferers in the world have often been its benefactors. Let no present affliction hinder such usefulness as is in our power. Let us give roses though we touch thorns.

"Death conducts to judgment, and the one who comes through judgment with Christ, finds home, the real home."

SOURCES

- Family documents passed from D.B. Turney to his son George J. Turney to his daughter Lois Turney White to me (sermons, letters, poems, articles, pamphlets, family bible, licenses, photos etc.)

- Eugenics Record # 3949 Carnegie Institution of Washington, Record of Family Traits, the Turney family info by George J. Turney, submitted 31 May 1913; rev 30 May 1927

- Thirty original D.B. Turney hand-written sermons, bound and indexed, but undated

- A 70,000- word transcript of March 1909 debate in Keens, Illinois

- D.B. Turney's published pamphlets: "The Mythifying Theory" (1872), "Peep into Psychomancy" (1878), "Mode of Baptism" (1887, 1894)

- Conference journals and histories from M.P. churches in IL, IA, IN, MO and WV'

- The Methodist Reporter, national paper of M.P. Church, 1880-1926. Three dozen articles by and about D.B. Turney- accessed in Shipman Library, Adrian, MI and online

- 250 newspaper articles about Turney- accessed online; found in libraries; family copies

- Federal Census records from 1850 through 1920; IA special census 1895

- Church histories from many of the 60+ local churches he served

- State libraries; county libraries, historical and genealogy societies

- Cemetery records- IL, WIS, WA, OH

- Various books about the period, including:
    Dary, David *The Oregon Trail: An American Saga.* Knopf
       (2004)
    Peters, Arthur King *Seven Trails West.* Abbeville Press (1946

- King James version of the Bible

CHAPTER NOTES

Below are some of the sources I used in writing D.B. Turney's story. Abbreviations include: MP= Methodist Protestant Church and ME= Methodist Episcopal Church.

Chapter 1 The Oregon Trail 1861

Family letters provided the departure and arrival dates for the family journey

from Fairfield, IL to Olympia, WA.

Hewitt, R.H. *Dundee, IL to Olympia*, Dogwood Press (1863)

Hornbuckle, Chuck and Suzanne. *Fort Vancouver to Puget Sound* (1916). 22

McLynn, Frank. *Wagons West.* Grove Press (2002)

Washingtonhistory.org *Johnson's Washington Oregon Map 1861* No.1999.0.5

Washington State Historical Society Tacoma, WA

Chapter 2 Olympia, Washington 1861-1862

Family copy of letter written by L. Jay S. Turney, acting governor (9 Sept 1861)

Gates, Chrarles M. *Messages of Washington Territorial Governors, 1854-1889,* U. of Wash Publications, Vol 12 (Aug 1940). 92 ff

Oregon Historical Society, scrapbook of newspaper clippings and original letter from William Pickering, Olympia WA to J.W. Stephenson (26 July, 1862).

The Washington Standard 24 Aug 1861. 2, 14 Sept 1861. 2 House oath of office.

Howe, Hubert. *History of Washington, Idaho and Montana.* Bancroft (1890). 219

Chapter 3 Walla Walla, Washington 1863-1865

The Washington Standard 27 June 1863. 2; 15 Aug 1863. 2 Election.

Chapter 4 Salem, Oregon Fall 1865

Wallamet University Catalogue for the Academic Year 1865-6, Salem, OR Statesman Book and Job Office (1866). 12

Hotel Fires in Salem Salem, Oregon Public Library Online Project. 2-3

Oregon Statesman 19 Nov 1866. 2, 10 Dec 1866. 2

Chapter 5 Oregon City, Oregon 1868-1869

The New Northwest 6 Oct 1876. 2

Weekly Oregon Statesman (Salem, OR) 12 Aug 1887. 7

The Washington Standard (Olympia, WA) 31 Oct 1868. 2

Weekly Corvallis Gazette, Wm B. Carter, Ed. 15 Aug 1868. 2

Willamette Valley, Oregon Death records, 1836-2006. 323-325

Original M.E. Exhorter's License for Daniel B. Turney (17 Jan 1869) signed by George Roork.

Corvallis Gazette-Times (Corvallis, OR) The following dates and pages: 7 Aug 1869 .3, 28 Aug 1869 .2, 25 Sept 1869 .2, 2 Oct 1869 .1

Chapter 6 Sacramento to Chicago Aug. 1869

Chapter 7 Chicago, Illinois Aug. 30, 1869

Prohibition National Committee (U.S.) records 1872-1972. 8 linear feet of minutes, clippings, papers etc. Bentley Hist Library, U. of Mich. Call No. 86124 Bt 2

Chapter 8 Benton, Illinois 1869-1870

Original D.B. Turney handwritten sermons. 307, 11-15

Chapter 9 Woodburn and Mediapolis, Illinois 1870- 1872

Turney, D.B. *The Mythifying Theory* or *Abraham Lincoln a Myth.*B. O. Jones, Book and Job Printer, Metropolis, IL (1872)

Southern IL Conference Journal of the M E Church (1870). 15,17,19

Southern IL Conf Journal of the M E Church (27 Sept- 2Oct 1871). 5, 9, 20, 30

Southern IL Conf Journal of the M E Church (1872). 12

Chapter 10 Cairo, Illinois 1872- 1873

The Cairo Bulletin. Cairo, IL The following dates and pages:

27 Sept 1871. 4, 28 Sept 1971. 4, 1 Oct 1871.4, 27 Oct 1871.4, 18 May 1872.4 11 July 1872.4, 13 Aug 1872.2, 15 Aug 1872.4, 10 Sept 1872.3, 1 Oct 1872.4

30 Oct 1872,4, 1 Nov 1872.4;

Evolution debate-19 Feb 1873. 4, 20 Feb 187.4, 21 Feb 1873. 4, 2 Mar 1873. 4, 10 May 1873. 2, 19 Mar 1873.4, 10 May 1873. 2, 14 May 1873.4, 28 May 1873.8,

13 May 1873. 4, 14 May 1873. 3, 6 June 1873. 1

Chapter 11 Paris and Grandview, Illinois 1873-1875

The Cairo Bulletin, Cairo, IL. 14 Dec 1873. 3, 8 April 1874. 4

The Chicago Daily Tribune (Chicago, IL) 19 June 1909 F.W. Jones, editor of the Cedar Rapids (IA) Tribune, wrote about how D.B. Turney had rescued him 36 years before in Cairo, IL.

S. IL Annual Conf ME Journal (24 Sept 1874). 138, 139

Wayne Co. Press (IL) 6 May 1875

Daily Recorder. 1875 General Conference, M P Church, Princeton, IL. 21-31 May 1875

Family scrapbook of newspaper clippings

Chapter 12 Bond County, Illinois 1875-1876

History of Bond County, IL 1882. Illinois Genealogy Trails. 31

Methodist Reporter (MP Church) 30 Oct 1875. 1

The Inter Ocean (Chicago, IL) 1 July 1876. 9

Chapter 13 Ohio Nov. 1876

Original probate court license to do weddings, Richland Co., OH (1 Jan 1877)

Cemetery index Richland Co, OH (30 April 1877) Box 2, Sect 1885, p T-2

Richland Shield and Banner 5 May 1877 Obituary for Turney stillborn baby boy.

Mansfield, OH newspaper 26 July 1877. 3

Mansfield courthouse sermon based on Turney handwritten sermon. 151; reported in *The Methodist Reporter* 6 Oct 1877. 2

Chapter 14 West Virginia Fall 1877

Turney, D.B. *A Peep into Psychomancy* or *The Pro and Con of Modern Spiritism.* Mansfield, OH Herald Steam Printing Est (1880)

The Wheeling Daily Intelligencer 31 Aug 1878. 1

Minutes of WV Conf of MP Church (27 Aug 1879). 1, 2, 4, 5, 7, 8, 10, 16, 17

Marriage Book, Ritchie Co., WV (12 Nov 1879). 41 D.B. Turney, officiating minister.

The Methodist Recorder (MP Church) 21 Feb 1880. 6

The Methodist Recorder (Official Organ of the Methodist Protestant Church, published in Pittsburgh, PA) D.B. Turney's weekly articles "Moral Meditations" were featured on the front page from 15 May 1880. 1 thru 3 July 1880. 1

The Methodist Recorder 9 Oct 1880. 5

Proceedings of the 26th Session of the WV Annual Conference of the Methodist Protestant Church (25-30 Aug 1880). 3, 7, 9, 11-13, 19, 21, 23, 25

Chapter 15 Washington, D.C. Fall 1880

1881 City Directory, Washington D.C. listed Turney, Rev. Daniel Braxton *"The National Cyclopaedia of American Biography, V 1.* 206. Ninth Street M P Church, Washington D.C. dedicated 19 July 1835.

Original letter from L. Jay S. Turney to Daniel Braxton Turney (11 Mar 1881).

The Inter Ocean (Chicago, IL) 4 March 1881. 2

Benton, IL United Methodist Church membership book 1881 death entry

Chapter 16 Lawrence County, Illinois Fall 1881

McCormick, D.M. *History of Edwards, Lawrence and Wabash Counties, IL* (1883)

Lawrence Co. Russellville M P Church Circuit history. 184-185

Benton, IL land deed from Elizabeth Turney to Daniel B. Turney of Lawrence Co., IL 24 Dec 1881

The Cairo Bulletin 10 Jan 1882. 4, 25 Jan 1882. 4

M.P. Year Book 1882 lists D. B. Turney of Birds Station, IL as President of the Southern Il Conference held 5 Sept 1882 in Paris, IL. 40

Chapter 17 Northern Illinois Nov. 1882

The Pantagraph (Bloomington, IL) 24 Nov 1882.3 Turneys arrived in Holder, IL.

The Pleasant Grove Cemetery, Old Town Township in McLean Co., IL- burial site of Elizabeth Turney- Old Section, row 10, section B 48

MP Conference Journal, Southern IL 1883-1889 1883 Journal- La Harpe Station, supplied by D. B. Turney. 24

La Harpe, IL 1836-1986 Sesquicentennial. 30-31

The Methodist Protestant Yearbook for 1884. 43, 58 D, B. Turney, representative.

The Cairo Bulletin (Cairo, IL) 28 May 1884. 4

MP Conference Journal IL 1883-1889 1884 Journal. 22 D.B. Turney, without appt.

MP Conference Journal IL 1883-1889 1885 Journal. 22 D.B. Turney, New Bedford.

The Methodist Recorder 6 Feb 1886 N IL President's report. 10 "D.B. released from New Bedford and appointed to Spring Valley and Farm Ridge."

The Ottawa Free Trader (Ottawa, IL) 24 July 1886. 5 "Rev. D. B. Turney, of Peru, was made Secretary" at Prohibition Convention.

Chicago Tribune. 6 Aug 1886. 3 "The Prohibition Congressional Convention for the eighth Dist...nominated Daniel B. Turney, a Methodist clergyman of Peru."

Minutes of North IL Conf of MP Church (1886). 25 D. B. Turney appointed to Spring Valley; L.L. Turney to Farm Ridge.

Ottawa Free Trader. 30 Oct 1866. 2 Daniel B. Turney, prohibition candidate.

The Pantagraph (Bloomington, IL) 2 Mar 1887. 3, 24 May 1887. 4, 24 Sept 1887. 3

The Winfield Tribune (Winfield, KS) 3 Sept 1887.2 Turney kind deed.

Minutes of N. IL MP Conf, 1887.28 D. B. Turney appointed to Lincoln and Natrona Ct; L.L. Turney left in the hands of president.

The Times 12 Jan 1888. 3 Daniel B. Turney's political roots.

The Inter Ocean (Chicago) 24 Mar 1888.16 Turney- Abraham Lincoln of Prohibition Party.

Wichita Eagle (Wichita, KS) 3 Feb 1888. 4

Minutes of N. IL Conf of MP Church, 1888. 13 D.B. Turney, to be employed; L. L. Turney, removed by letter.

The Fort Wayne Sentinel (IND) 22 Sept 1888. 2 Turney blackguard story.

Minutes of N IL MP Conf. 1889. 16 Turney, of Lincoln, IL- Conference Missionary.

Decatur Daily Republican (Decatur, IL) 7 Dec 1889. 1 D. B. Turney moves to Iowa.

Chapter 18 Bennett, Iowa Dec. 1889- 1891

Tipton Advertiser (IA) 12 Dec 1889. 3, 26 Dec 1889. 3, 20 Feb 1890.3

The Cedar Co. (IA) Historical Review, Supplement to 1959 Yearbook. The Cedar Co Historical Soc. Tipton, IA (1959). 4-5, 27

The Algona Republican (IA) 17 Sept 1890.6 Iowa Prohibitionists.

The New Era (Humeston, IA) 19 Nov 1890. 4 Turney in buggy accident.

The Chicago Tribune. 11 June 1891. 5 Turney, temporary chair IA Prohibitionists.

Bennett, Iowa and Inland Township, A History by Verl L. Lekwa (1983). 220-221

Chapter 19 Central Iowa 1891-1895

Iowa Conf Journal of MP Church- 1891.33, 1892.34, 1893.28, 1894.28, 1895.33

The Indianapolis News. 25 Oct 1893. 1 Turney resigns from Rhodes, IA MP church.

Kingery, Karlene (ed) *Settlement to Centennial, Marshall Co, IA 1849-1982*. 15, 56

Nation-wide ad Paine's Celery Compound ad campaign 26 Oct 1895 in scores of papers:

> *The Evening Express*, Los Angeles; *The Wilmington Daily Republican*; *The Pensacola News*; *Akron Daily Democrat*; *The Dispatch*, Moline, etc.

Chapter 20 Milton, Iowa 1895-1897

Milton Herald (IA) 28 March 1895 through 27 Oct 1897- Forty-seven references to D.B. Turney or family discovered in Iowa Hist Soc newspaper microfilm.

History of Milton (IA) Van Buren Co. Historical Society, transcribed by Richard Lowe (1969). MP Church. 2, 6

The Quill. 10 Sept 1896. "Rev. Daniel Boone Turnkey of Milton Iowa" is criticized.

Minutes of Missouri Annual Conf of the Methodist Protestant Church: Turney transfers in 3-7 Oct 1896. 9; transfers out 8-11 Sept 1897. 15

Chapter 21 Indiana and Eastern Illinois Oct. 1897- 1900

DePauw University Archives- Indiana MP pastoral appointments 1897-1900.

Historic Map Works- map of Brouilett's Creek Township, Item US48729 from Edgar County 1910, published by Geo. A. Ogle and Co.

1900 Federal Census, Edgar Co., IL, Brouilett's Creek Twp. 13 June 1900, line 80

Gilbert, Hilah Scott. *Prairie Progress, Brouilett's Creek Tp Schools. 42*

Chapter 22 Effingham, Illinois Fall 1900

The Cairo Bulletin (IL) 10 March 1875. 2 Turney's traveling attire.

Effingham Democrat 16 May 1902 Austin College Commencement preview.

Original letter from wife Emma, in Effingham, to Dan (30 May 1902)

Effingham Democrat 6 June 1902, 13 June 1902, 20 June 1902 Austin College.

Feldhake, Hilda E.(ed*). Effingham Co. IL, Past and Present.* The Effingham

Regional Historical Society (1968). 305 Ada Kepley, prohibition.

The Decatur Herald (IL) 6 Dec 1902.3. 12 May 1903.6 J.E.Z. Turney.

The Methodist Recorder 10 Oct 1903 Turney's debate with Professor Macy. 24 Oct 1903. 14-15 Turney's S. IL President's report.

Chicago Tribune 30 July 1904. 4 Prohibitionist Turney Grieves for Miles.

*Republican (*Salem, IL) 26 Oct 1905 Turney debates "the Latter-day Saints".

Journal Gazette (Mattoon, IL) 26 Dec 1905 Turney didn't win the farm.

The Inter Ocean (Chicago) 3 June 1906. 16 "J.E.Z. Turney...rare poetic gifts".

Freeport Journal-Standard (IL) 3 May 1907 D.B. Turney endorsed for president.

The Washington Times (DC) 20 June 1907. 5 Turney criticizes Roosevelt's behavior.

Greensboro Daily News (NC) 18 July 1907.1 Carrie Nation endorses Turney.

Brookville Democrat (IND) 8 Aug 1907 Turney criticizes Roosevelt.

The Decatur Herald (IL) 22 Sept 1907. 16 Turney quote: "...local option is too local and too optional. A national disease needs a national remedy."

The Daily Free Press (Carbondale, IL) 8 Nov 1907.1 Wins TN shooting contest.

Chapter 23 Decatur, Illinois Nov. 1907

The Decatur Herald (IL) 21 Nov 1907. 5, 25 Nov 1907. 4. Turney moves to Decatur.

2 Feb 1908. 20 Possible candidate for presidency lives in Decatur.

2 May 1908. 1 Decatur man named for the White House.

The Daily Review (Decatur, IL) 2 Feb 1908. 20 Turney needs money.

2 May 1908. 1 Turney is named for presidency.

The Argus (Rock Island, IL) 2 May 1908. 6 United Christian Party.

The Davenport Democrat (IA) 3 May 1908 W. J. Bryan declines U.C. nomination.

The McHenry Plaindealer (IL) 14 May 1908. 8 Turney, a bargain president.

The Decatur Herald (IL) 17 May 1908. 13 Turney letter outlines his principles.

19 May 1908. 6 Candidate Turney attacks socialism.

2 June 1908. 6 Turney writes open letter to William Jennings Bryan.

5 June 1908. 6 Turney refuses Prohibition nomination without Coffin.

12 June 1908. 12 Turney indorsed by Equal Rights Party.

12 June 1908. 12 Turney answers a question about prosperity.

The Daily Free Press (Carbondale, IL) 8 June 1908. 2 United Christian platform.

The Decatur Herald (IL) 23 July 1908. 12 Turney bans corporation money.

25 July 1908. 5 Turney campaign tour begins in Springfield, Mo.

Springfield Mo Republican 31 July 1908. 1 Parson believes he will be president.

Natchez Democrat (MISS) 6 Sept 1908. 2 United Christian party convention confusion.

The Decatur Herald (IL) 29 Aug 1908. Son George J. Turney interviewed.

6 Sept 1908. 1 Turney's march through the south.

The pre-election newspaper interview based on Turney's article published in *The Methodist Reporter* 16 Jan 1886. 5

The Decatur Herald (IL) 5 Nov 1908. 10 Turney pleased with his showing on Nov 3.

Republican (Salem, IL) 26 Nov 1908. 3 Presidential votes in Illinois.

Republican-Northwestern (Belvidere, IL) 15 Dec 1908. 5 D.B. threatens to leave party.

The Decatur Daily Review (IL) 30 Dec 1908. 10 Dan calls party leader's blockheads.

Chapter 24 Keen, Illinois (Debate) March 1909

Illinois State Historical Library, Springfield, IL. #90568 Complete transcript of three-day debate, 70,000 plus words.

Chapter 25 Decatur, Illinois 1909-1913

The Decatur Herald (IL) 18 Mar 1909.1 Turney to debate in Ohio.

4 April 1909. 23 Turney envisions an airship imitating bird flight.

5 April 1909. 2 Turney, M.P. president heads for Clark Center today.

24 June 1909. 10 Turney in Iowa at sick son's bedside.

15 July 1909. 7 D.B. Turney to preach at Central Park next Sunday.

27 Nov 1909. 5 Polemic returns after several months in southern IL.

Marshalltown Republican 24 Dec 1909 Obituary for John Edwin Zuriel Turney.

http:/findagrave.com J.E.Z. Turney died 14 Dec 1909; buried in Maricopa, AZ.

New Christian Bible Study (webpage)- John 11:25 Esperanto

The Daily Review (Decatur, IL) 18 Mar 1910. 7 Turney on enumerators' list.

The Decatur Herald (IL) 20 May 1910.2 Turney, conf president and census enumerator.

The Topeka Daily Capital (KS) 9 June 1910 Who is Daniel Braxton Turney?

The Daily Review (Decatur, IL) 23 Jan 1911. 10 Turney's eight-day baptism debate.

The Decatur Herald (IL) 10 June 1911. 5 Turney's short acceptance letter.

4 July 1911. 3 D.B. Turney opens national campaign in Mount Vernon, IL.

Chicago Tribune (IL) 27 Sept 1864. 1 Mass political meeting in Benton, IL, led by Braxton Parish (Turney's grandfather), was model for Turney's rally.

The Sun (New York, NY) 17 May 1912. 10 D. B. Turney Beats Roosevelt.

The Daily Review (Decatur, IL) 8 April 1912. 16 Teddy Roosevelt in Decatur.

The Rock Island Argus (IL) 1 May 1912. 5 United Christians nominate Turney.

The Daily Review (Decatur, IL) 7 May 1912 Candidate Turney worn out by strain.

14 June 1912. 14 Edlyn Sleeter weds George J. Turney.

The Decatur Herald (IL) 14 Sept 1912. 3 Turney is fraternal delegate to ME Conf.

27 Nov 1912.2 Rev. and Mrs. Daniel Turney will move to Washington, D.C.

Chapter 26 Washington, D.C. Fall 1913-1914

Family records- D.B. Turney had an assigned table at Library of Congress, D.C.

1 Feb 1913 through spring; 4 Nov 1913 until 1 Aug 1914.

The Daily Review (Decatur, IL) 27 Aug 1913.3 S. IL MP Conf and book promo.

17 Sept 1913 Turney elected to S. IL MP church positions; returns to DC.

The Methodist Recorder 17 Oct 1914.7 Turney article quoted at grandson's birth.

Chapter 27 Decatur, Illinois 1915-1926

Journal of the General Conf of the M P Church, 19-26 May 1916. 7 IL delegate.

Original letter from his brother Rev. Leander Turney (30 Dec 1916).

Decatur Herald (IL) 22 Mar 1917. 6 Turney claims victory in Michigan debate.

15 Sept 1917. 8 Turney appointed polemic and evangelist.

Yearbook of the MP Church 1918. 160, 175 S. IL Conf Steward and Polemic.

The Decatur Daily Review (IL) 31 Dec 1918. 10 Chairs Million Dollar campaign.

11 June 1919. 6 D.B. Turney's pedigree; possible presidential nomination.

23 Oct 1919. 16 Turney enters debate in Kentucky.

Pittsburgh Post-Gazette (PA) 25 May 1920. 1 Report on Methodist Protestant Church General Conference. D.B. Turney of Illinois Conference made a resolution.

The Decatur Herald (IL) 5 June 1920. 3 Turney reports on Greensboro Genl. Conf.

4 July 1920. 6 D.B. Turney gives up his hopes for presidency.

The Methodist Reporter 16 Oct 1920. 314 *Why Do We Sleep?* 17 verse poem by Turney.

Minutes of S. IL Conf of Methodist Protestant Church, 1922. 42-43, 46-48. D.B. Turney, chair of faculty instruction; preached Memorial Sermon.

The Decatur Daily Review (IL) 6 April 1923. 16 Turney attends Oglesby burial.

The Decatur Herald (IL) 22 April 1923. 20 Friends shower Turney with birthday dollars.

IL State Archives, Springfield. Jacksonville State Hospital Records for Macon Co., IL- George J. Turney admitted 23 May 1923, discharged 16 Nov 1923.

The Decatur Herald (IL) 16 Sept 1923 Turney attends union conf of IL MP Church.

Minutes of IL Conf of MP Church, 9-14 Sept 1924. 1-6, 12-13 D.B. Turney, Press Reporter, Bd of Directors, Ch of Faculty of Instruction; 100% attendance.

Minutes of IL Conf of MP Church 1925. 1, 6 Dan's name listed, but he did not attend.

Minutes of IL Conf of MP Church 1926. 25 Daniel B. Turney's passing is noted. "Memorial service will be held Sunday afternoon."

Minutes of IL Conf of MP Church 24-28 Aug 1927. 59 Turney listed among "The Honored Dead 1926."

The Decatur Review (IL) 19 Jan 1926 D.B. Turney death notice

The Decatur Herald (IL) 20 Jan 1926 D.B. Turney dies; twice candidate for presidency.

The Methodist Recorder 27 Feb 1926. Cover, 2, 14, 15 Denominational tributes.

26 June 1926. 6 "The Fool Hath Said," poem by late D. B. Turney.

The Decatur Herald and Review (IL) 5 June 1966. 51 Decatur Diary: "Turney was probably one of Decatur's widest known citizens in his time."

Portrait, courtesy of *Decatur Herald and Review*

Made in the USA
Coppell, TX
22 February 2021